# ENCYCLOPEDIA OF MAMMALS

## VOLUME 16
### Wha–Zeb

MARSHALL CAVENDISH

NEW YORK • LONDON • TORONTO • SYDNEY

# RORQUALS

Rorquals belong to the family Balaenopteridae in the suborder Mysticeti, or baleen whales. Other baleen whales include:

**RIGHT WHALE**

**BOWHEAD WHALE**

**GRAY WHALE**

Art Wolfe/Tony Stone Worldwide

# GIGANTIC MAMMALS

### THE WHALE FAMILY CAN BOAST THE LARGEST ANIMAL ON EARTH, THE BLUE WHALE. ALL WHALES ARE FASCINATING, AND HUMANS CAN LEARN A GREAT DEAL FROM THESE HIGHLY INTELLIGENT GIANTS

The largest animal ever to live on our planet was not a dinosaur. In fact, it swims in the oceans today and is known as the blue whale. This vast creature weighs up to 210 tons, the equivalent of 2,500 adult humans. It is also known as the Sibbald's rorqual, for it is a member of the great-whale group called rorquals.

The blue whale holds many other records. It has the largest heart of any animal, the size of a small car. Its skeleton weighs 20 tons and its tongue 4.5 tons, in a mouth up to 19 ft (6 m) long. During its main feeding season, an average-sized whale can increase its weight by half—over 55 tons.

The blue whale is one of six species in the rorqual group or family Balaenopteridae. The others, in order of decreasing size, are the fin, humpback, sei, Bryde's, and minke whales. The word *rorqual* is derived from the Norse word *rørhval*, meaning "grooved whale." It refers to the

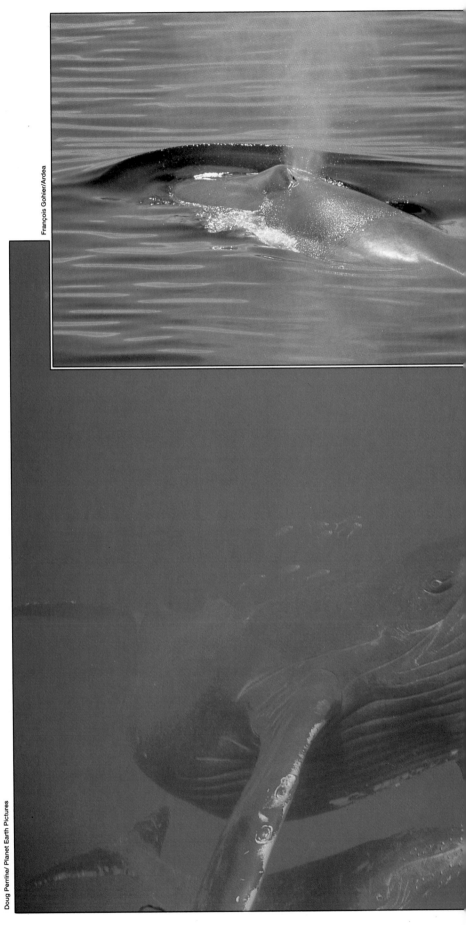

*The blue whale surfaces to blow. This powerful jet is expelled in a single column.*

François Gohier/Ardea

grooves or pleats along the throat, which allow enormous balloonlike expansion of the chin and throat skin when feeding, as the whale gulps in enough water to fill a swimming pool.

Rorquals, in turn, belong to the group of whales known as great, whalebone, or baleen whales. Other members are the three species of right whales and the gray whale of the Pacific. The baleen whales' common feature is the stringy plates and comblike fibers of baleen or whalebone, which hang from the roof of the mouth, where most mammals have their upper teeth. This curtain of baleen is a filter for straining food from seawater for, despite their tremendous bulk, rorquals do not eat large prey. Their victims are tiny—shrimplike krill and little fish, often smaller than a human finger.

### WARM-BLOODED ANIMALS

Whales are warm-blooded air-breathers that feed their babies on mother's milk. However, like fish, whales live their whole lives in the sea. They feed, mate, give birth, and suckle their young in the

> RORQUALS HAVE NO·TEETH. HOWEVER, THEY HAVE ADAPTED THEIR FEEDING MECHANISM TO TAKE IN ENORMOUS AMOUNTS OF PLANKTON AT ONE TIME

water. So they have evolved to look and swim like fish. Rorquals, especially, have lost virtually all body hair for the sake of streamlining, their front limbs have become flippers or pectoral fins, and their hind limbs have disappeared. They have a small dorsal fin set well to the rear and large tail flukes that are horizontal, as in all whales—unlike the vertical tails of fish.

Neither the dorsal fin nor the tail flukes have bones inside. However, there are bones in the flippers or "arms." Compared with other whales, rorquals have relatively small flippers—except for the humpback, which has the longest flippers, in proportion to body length, of any whale.

Rorquals do not dive to great depths to pursue their prey; neither do they use the sonar system of echolocation to pinpoint victims. Instead, they feed mainly in the surface waters, using the great sheets and combs of baleen or whalebone to sift planktonic organisms from the water. This filter-feeding ensures a constant and huge supply.

*A humpback whale with its characteristic flippers and "humped" back.*

Doug Perrine/ Planet Earth Pictures

Nevertheless, rorquals can stay submerged for many minutes. And they are far from silent. They produce noises or whale songs to communicate with each other over hundreds of miles.

The minke is the smallest of the rorquals, yet it is still some 33 ft (10 m) long and weighs around 8.8–11 tons. Coloration is dark or black at the front and tail and along the middle of the back, but gray-white on the upper flanks and around the underside. The minke has a single ridge on the top of its long head, 50–70 throat pleats, a prominent dorsal fin, a crosswise white stripe on each flipper, and proportionally large flukes. In each side of its straight mouth hang about 250–350 plates of baleen, each some 8 in (20 cm) long.

Minkes tend to stay in coastal temperate waters and often breach—or leap—right out of the water.

### MASSIVE FLIPPERS

The humpback also seems to like breaching, and falls back into the water with a tremendous splash. This rorqual is the third largest in the group, at 52–62 ft (16–19 m) in length and 44–66 tons in weight. It has the roundest body of the group, and a massive head adorned with protuberances, especially on the chin, lips, and forehead, as well as hair follicles, barnacles that have set up home there, and pests such as whale lice. There are only 15–20 throat grooves, but up to 400 baleen plates on either side of the upwardly bowed mouth.

The humpback's name derives from its slightly humped back. The enormous flippers, biggest of any whale, are up to one-third the length of the body. They are serrated or wavy on the leading edge, a feature that helps recognition at sea. The massive flippers are also covered with lumps and

## WHY SO BIG?

The great size of the rorquals is probably based on the need to conserve body heat in cold seas. Whales have a body temperature of about 97–100°F (36–38°C), much like humans. But they often swim in cold seas, with temperatures as low as 29°F (–1.7°C). Although water carries away body heat more effectively than air, this effect decreases with increasing size, because bigger objects have less surface area in proportion to their total volume, and heat is lost through the surface. So, a small animal with a high surface-to-volume ratio loses body heat far faster than a large animal with a low surface-to-volume ratio.

In addition, despite their size, the whales' ability to float in the water means that they are effectively weightless, so they are less limited by the effects of gravity.

Baleen whales also consume tiny plankton, so they are able to feed their great size without chasing prey—unlike a hunting carnivore.

As a result of these factors, whales have evolved to become even bigger. Whether this is continuing is not clear. We have not been measuring them long enough to find out.

# ANCESTORS

The cetaceans probably evolved from the condylarths, carnivorous hoofed land mammals, some 60 million years ago. Condylarths probably gave rise to ancestors of whales, the mesonychids.

Fossils of the mesonychids show that some had pointed fish-eating teeth. They could have given rise to the earliest whales, the Archaeoceti.

There were probably three groups of Archaeoceti. One was the Basilosauridae, which had front flippers, and its hind legs and hips had almost disappeared. It also had a streamlined body.

It may have given rise to the two modern suborders of whales: the Odontoceti, or toothed whales, and the Mysticeti, baleen whales, 30 million years ago.

barnacles. The tail flukes are very wide and have serrated trailing edges, another helpful feature for identification.

The coloration of the humpback is almost black above and almost white below, with specimens from southern seas appearing to have more white. The flippers are speckled and mottled dark and white on their upper sides, increasing toward the tips. Humpbacks live in all oceans, favoring tropical in winter and polar in summer, and they migrate farther than other rorquals. They also sing the most amazing songs to each other (see page 2333). ∎

# HUMPBACK WHALE

*Megaptera novaeangliae*
*(meg-AP-ter-ah no-vay-AN-glee-ay)*

**The humpback whale is the single species belonging to the genus Megaptera. It differs from all the other rorquals in its** **stoutness and huge flippers. The latter measure almost a third of the whale's body length and are serrated on the leading** **edge. Humpbacks also produce the most varied and the longest whale songs of any animal. These songs even vary annually.**

# THE RORQUAL WHALES' FAMILY TREE

*Baleen whales provide a fairly neat group for zoologists to classify. The baleen, or whalebone, is not found in any other animal and probably evolved through increased fringing of the gums or mouth roof in a single distant ancestor. The baleen group includes the right whales and the gray whale. There are six rorqual species, with the humpback being put in a separate genus from the other five.*

## MINKE WHALE  *Balaenoptera acutorostrata*
*(bal-en-OP-ter-ah ak-U-to-ro-STRA-tah)*

**The minke, or piked whale, is the smallest of all rorquals and can be distinguished by its** **pointed rostrum and a more rounded build than its relatives. Minkes are found** **worldwide, although rarely in the tropics. It is curious by nature and most likely to be seen.**

## FIN WHALE  *Balaenoptera physalus*
*(bal-en-OP-ter-ah FIE-sah-lus)*

**The fin whale is the second-largest member of this family, although probably the fastest of** **the great whales at up to 25 mph (40 km/h). It can be distinguished by its unique facial** **coloring: dark gray on the left-hand side and pale, almost white, on the right.**

TOOTHED WHALES

PORPOISES        DOLPHINS        LARGE WHALES

# BLUE WHALE

*Balaenoptera musculus*
*(bal-en-OP-ter-rah MUS-qu-lus)*

The blue whale is the largest animal the world has ever seen. Measuring an average 76 ft (23 m) for males and 82 ft (25 m) for females, these gigantic animals weigh between 83 and 143 tons (80,000 and 130,000 kg). They populate the Antarctic, North Atlantic, and North Pacific Oceans.

# SEI WHALE

*Balaenoptera borealis*
*(bal-en-OP-ter-rah bo-ray-AH-lis)*

The sei whale is a typical rorqual, with a flat head and streamlined body. In shape and color it resembles the blue whale. However, the dark gray coloring on its back and mottled coloring on its underside give it a very metallic look. Seis are found worldwide, although they avoid the coldest areas.

# BRYDE'S WHALE

*Balaenoptera edeni*
*(b. EE-den-eye)*

Bryde's whale is found in tropical waters throughout the world and is also called the tropical whale. It has around 300 baleen plates, which have stiff bristles, in its mouth. As a result, Bryde's whale tends to eat a great deal of fish rather than plankton. Bryde's whale is easily distinguished from other rorquals by the three lengthwise ridges on the top of its head.

*BALAENOPTERA*

RIGHT WHALES

GRAY WHALES

BALEEN WHALES

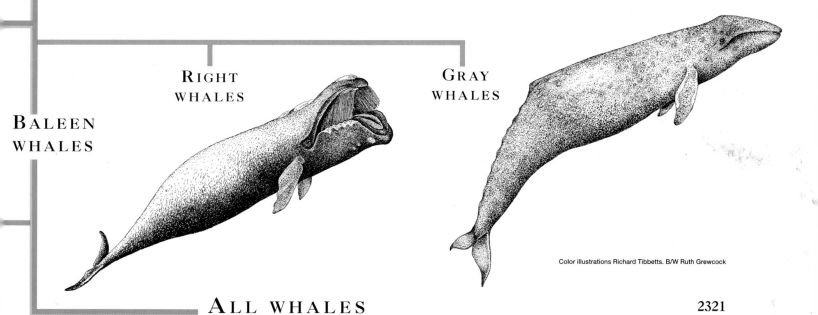

Color illustrations Richard Tibbetts. B/W Ruth Grewcock

ALL WHALES

# A N A T O M Y :
## THE BLUE WHALE

**THE FLIPPERS,**

or pectoral fins, are supported by bones equivalent to those in your arm and hand but are used as paddles. They help with maneuvering at slow speeds.

In length, the blue whale is the equivalent of seventeen adult humans placed head to toe; its tongue alone weighs as much as an elephant. It is three times as long as the smallest rorqual in its family, the minke whale.

**THROAT PLEATS**

or grooves allow the slightly elastic skin to balloon out as the whale gulps in water. Then they fold back and retract as the water is expelled.

**EYES AND EARS**

are barely visible. The tiny eyes see only to the side. There are no external ears, although baleens hear very well.

**THE BLOWHOLES**

are the whale's nostrils, which have migrated during evolution from the front to the top of the head. There are two blowholes side by side, producing one blow of steamy, breathed-out air. The blowholes of baleen whales have some sense of smell.

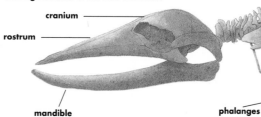

**BLUE**

**FIN**

**SEI**

The maximum lengths of the rorquals are:
Blue whale 110 ft (34 m);
Fin whale 88.5 ft (27 m);
Humpback whale 49 ft (15 m);
Sei whale 65 ft (20 m);
Bryde's whale 46 ft (14 m);
Minke whale 33 ft (10 m).

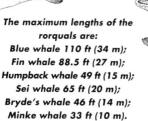

**BRYDE'S**

**HUMPBACK**

**MINKE**

**X**

**R A Y**

**SKELETON**
The typical mammal skeleton has been greatly modified to the totally aquatic lifestyle. The neck bones (cervical vertebrae) are short, thick, and fused together. The ribs are slim and delicate. The chest, hip, and tail sections of the backbone are hardly distinguishable from one another.

vertebrae

cranium

rostrum

mandible

phalanges

**FRONT LIMBS**
The shoulder and arm bones are short but wide and strong. The hand and finger bones splay out and support the flipper.

**SKULL**
Unlike the skulls of toothed whales, the baleen whale's skull is symmetrical. The upper part is extended into a long, beaklike rostrum that supports the upper mouth and baleen.

X-ray illustrations Elisabeth Smith. B/W illustrations Ruth Grewcock.

## BLUE WHALE HEAD

Like all rorquals, the blue whale has distinct throat grooves or pleats (below left), which distend when the huge mouth is full of water (below).

### CLASSIFICATION

GENUS: *BALAENOPTERA*

SPECIES: *MUSCULUS*

### SIZE

TOTAL LENGTH/MALE: AVERAGE 76 FT (23 M), EXCEPTIONALLY OVER 98 FT (30 M)

TOTAL LENGTH/FEMALE: AVERAGE 82 FT (25 M), EXCEPTIONALLY OVER 108 FT (33 M)

WEIGHT/MALE: 77–110 TONS

WEIGHT/FEMALE: 110–165 TONS, RECORD POSSIBLY 210 TONS

TOTAL LENGTH AT BIRTH: 23–26 FT (7–8 M)

### COLORATION

GENERALLY BLUE-GRAY, VARYING FROM LIGHT BLUE TO SLATE GRAY, LIGHTER MOTTLED PATCHES AND FIN UNDERSIDES. MAY BE BLOTCHED YELLOWISH IN COLDER WATERS WITH ALGAL GROWTHS

### FEATURES

LARGEST ANIMAL OF ALL TIME

VERY SLIM IN PROPORTION TO LENGTH COMPARED WITH MANY OTHER WHALES

AS HEAVY AS SIXTY TYPICAL ZOO ELEPHANTS OR FIVE TRACTOR TRAILERS

AS LONG AS SEVENTEEN ADULTS LYING HEAD TO TOE

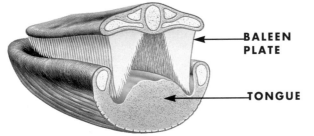

## STREAMLINING

means that the body and tail stock are smoothly contoured. Even the genitals and mammary glands are hidden in folds of skin.

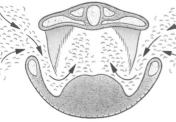

## THE SKIN

is smooth and hairless. This allows water to slip easily past it. Under the skin is a thick layer of fatty blubber, which acts as an insulating blanket to help retain body warmth.

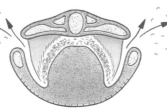

**BALEEN PLATE**

**TONGUE**

## FEEDING ACTION

The whale opens its mouth and water with plankton is drawn in (above). Then its tongue expands and water is extracted, leaving just the plankton (right).

## BALEEN PLATE IN DETAIL

The above cross section shows the many layers of baleen plates in the whale's mouth. These are very effective in trapping tiny plankton.

## THE FLUKES

measure over 13 ft (4 m) from tip to tip, but they are relatively small for the blue whale's body size. They thrash up and down to power it through the water and are also used to smack the surface for sound-signaling.

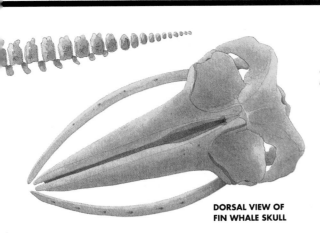

**DORSAL VIEW OF FIN WHALE SKULL**

### LOWER JAW

The lower jawbones (mandibles) are set widely apart and loosely joined to the skull, so that they can move freely as the whale fills its mouth with water to take in tiny krill—its staple diet.

**DORSAL VIEW OF BLUE WHALE SKULL**

**DORSAL VIEW OF HUMPBACK WHALE SKULL**

Color illustrations Steve Kingston

# OCEAN WANDERERS

**PEOPLE HAVE SEEN, WATCHED, PURSUED, HUNTED, EATEN, AND UTILIZED RORQUALS FOR THOUSANDS OF YEARS, YET WE STILL KNOW RELATIVELY LITTLE ABOUT THEIR BEHAVIOR**

W hales are hard to study scientifically at close quarters. They are difficult to find in the vast oceans, they live mostly beneath the waves, and they are usually on the move, which makes direct observation difficult. Also, whaling has made them rare and so even less likely to be encountered.

Behavioral profiles have been assembled from folklore, historical accounts, the observations and records of whalers, as well as by modern scientific techniques such as surface observations, marking, sonar and aerial surveys, radio tracking, shore and boat sightings, song recordings, strandings, and even satellite pictures.

In general, most is known about humpbacks. When not on migration they tend to live near coastlines, where there are more vessels and they are seen more often. They also feed more at the surface than other rorquals and tend to rest at the surface, roll, flipper- and tail-smack, and breach (leap) more frequently.

### PROBLEMS OF SPOTTING SPECIES

Rorquals feed, rest, and travel by day and by night. However, they occasionally take time off to bask in the midday sun. Their swimming abilities and active habits make them difficult even for modern boats to follow. The sei whale is the fastest of the group, reaching maximum speeds of 31 mph (50 km/h), and is able to cruise for many hours at 8 mph (13 km/h). The minke, also known as the piked whale, can sprint at over 28 mph (45 km/h) and cruise at 6–7.5 mph (10–12 km/h). Fin whales have been recorded as covering 19 miles (30 kilometers) in one hour and swimming for several hours at 10–12.4 mph (16–20 km/h).

It may also be difficult to distinguish one rorqual species from another. Clues are the overall size of the animal (which is difficult to estimate in a featureless ocean), the shape and position of the dorsal fin, the size and shape of the flukes, the surfacing method, and the blow.

The blow is the spout of stale air breathed out from the blowholes as the whale surfaces. It comes from the whale's lungs, so it is warm and moist. As it meets the cold air outside, its moisture condenses into a steamy jet. The blow also carries droplets of mucus from the lining of the whale's nasal passages, windpipe, and lungs, plus water that has leaked in through the closed blowholes while the whale was submerged.

The steamy fountain of the blow is tallest—about 30 ft (9 m)—and almost vertical in the blue whale. The fin whale's blow is up to 20 ft (6 m) high and shaped like a narrow upturned cone. The minke's blow is only 6.5–10 ft tall (2 to 3 m) and

ANT/NHPA

David E. Myers/Tony Stone Worldwide

*The impressive tail of the blue whale emerges from the sea as the gentle giant dives underwater* (above).

**KEY FACTS**

● Scientists studying the ocean bottom have recorded surprising numbers of decaying carcasses of rorquals and other baleen whales. They have come to the conclusion that rorquals are important in the overall ecology of the seas, not only when alive, but also when dead. Their huge bodies feed many scavenging animals. In turn, these are hunted by predators, thus returning the concentrated nutrients in the rorquals to the ocean food chains.

● Some slowly decomposing, seabed rorqual carcasses support colonies of unique organisms—bacteria, worms, and shellfish—that previously have been found only around deep-sea hydrothermal vents. Warm, sulfur-rich gases and chemicals bubble up through these vents, from deep in Earth's crust.

more of a cloud, quickly dispersed by a light wind.

The frequency of the blow is another helpful clue. When resting, the blue whale breathes out about once every two minutes. After a dive or a chase, this rises to five or six times in one minute as the great mammal pants.

### ROUTINES AND HABITS
Most rorquals have a well-defined yearly routine. All except Bryde's whale, also called the tropical whale, have their main feeding season in summer, in the cold but nutrient-rich polar waters that swarm with life. They can put on many tons in body weight. In winter they migrate to warmer subtropical waters to rest, calve (give birth), and mate, and feed only occasionally.

Rorquals are reasonably sociable and form loose groups and associations. But these are nowhere nearly as well defined, organized, or permanent as, for example, the pods of killer whales.

In many respects of their lifestyle, rorquals are not untypical of mammals. They court and communicate by sound and occasionally by vision, as the males sing and display and even battle with each other for the right to mate with females. The cow-calf (mother-baby) associations are the only strong, relatively long-lasting ones. ■

*Active and gregarious, this pair of humpbacks put on a spectacular display of acrobatics.*

# HABITATS

Tui de Roy/Oxford Scientific Films

Rorquals are restless ocean wanderers, but most species have a pattern to their travels. They undertake migrations between two optimum types of sites: those for feeding and those for breeding.

In general, the feeding areas are the cold oceans of the far north and south, around the Arctic and Antarctic. The temperatures may be low, but ocean currents and upwellings from the stirred-up sea floor sweep in huge amounts of nutrients.

The breeding areas are in the warmer tropics and subtropics. There is much less rorqual food here. But the whales rest, use little energy to stay warm, and survive for weeks on the many tons of fatty reserves accumulated and stored from the summer feed.

### NEVER TO MEET

Traveling between these two areas means that rorquals undertake some of the longest migrations of any animal. This is made possible by their huge size and powerful swimming.

Each spring in the Northern Hemisphere, many rorquals head north from the subtropics, toward the Arctic and the summer flush of food. At the same time, at the other end of the globe, the long Antarctic summer is just ending, and the rorquals of the Southern Hemisphere now take their turn in returning to subtropical waters.

Six months later the travels are reversed, with the Northern Hemisphere whales heading south and the southern ones doing the same. Since few rorquals actually cross the equator or mix with their counterparts from the other hemisphere, this.

*A Bryde's whale basks in the warm sea off the coast of Baja California, Mexico. This species of whale prefers to stay close to shore and is found only in tropical or subtropical waters.*

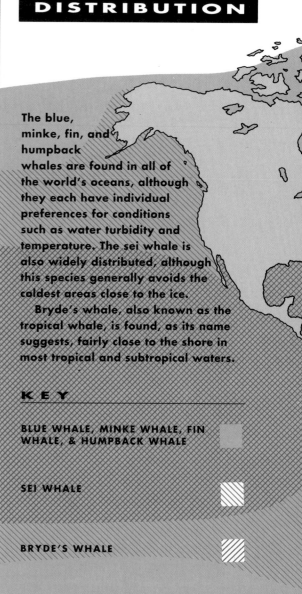

## DISTRIBUTION

The blue, minke, fin, and humpback whales are found in all of the world's oceans, although they each have individual preferences for conditions such as water turbidity and temperature. The sei whale is also widely distributed, although this species generally avoids the coldest areas close to the ice.

Bryde's whale, also known as the tropical whale, is found, as its name suggests, fairly close to the shore in most tropical and subtropical waters.

### KEY

BLUE WHALE, MINKE WHALE, FIN WHALE, & HUMPBACK WHALE

SEI WHALE

BRYDE'S WHALE

## inSIGHT

### HOW DO RORQUALS NAVIGATE?

Rorquals and other whales make journeys of thousands of miles through oceans that seem featureless and unvarying to our eyes. They also stop off en route to feed in the same inlets and bays each year. How do they know where, and when, to go?

The answer begins with the fact that, unlike humans, rorquals do not rely on their eyes. Studies have revealed the following:

Whale skin can detect subtle changes in water temperature and flow, indicating currents.

Gravitational force varies subtly around the Earth, depending on the presence of rocks of different density, mountains, and valleys. Whales may be able to sense this.

Many animals have tiny fragments of magnetic minerals in or near their brains, which provide a built-in compass to detect Earth's magnetic field. Such minerals occur in whales, though how the magnetic sense could work is not clear.

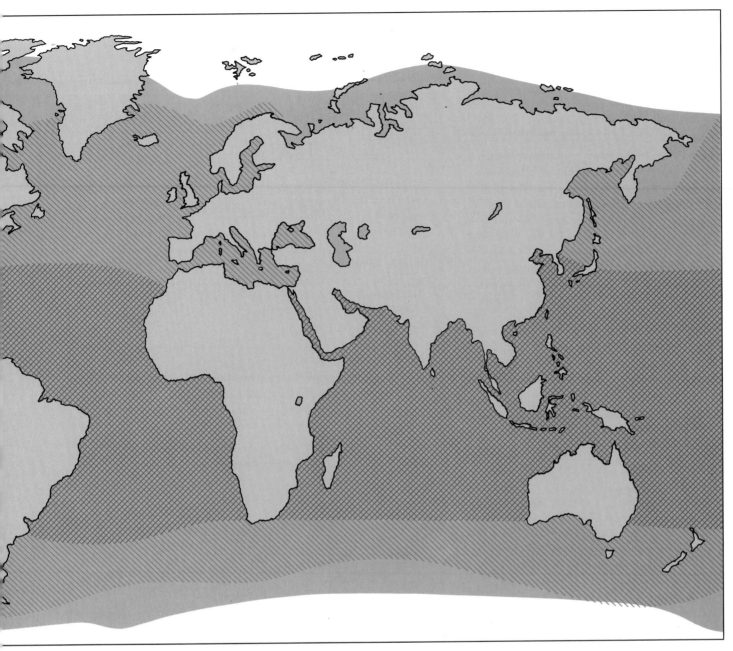

*A humpback whale in Alaska makes an early
morning splash with its enormous pectoral fin.*

means there are separate northern and southern
populations of most species. The populations are
further restricted east and west by landmasses,
into subpopulations or stocks, mainly in the
Atlantic, Pacific, and Indian Oceans.

### PREFERRED HABITATS

Within this general pattern, each rorqual species
has its preferred migrations and habitats, where it
finds just the right balance of food supplies, water
temperature, and currents.

    The blue whale lives mainly along the edges of
continental shelves and out in the open ocean. It is
rarely spotted near land and seems equally at
home in the steamy tropics or right next to the
polar ice caps. The fin whale is probably the most
wide-ranging rorqual, seen in all of the world's

## (in) SIGHT

### ONLY THREE LINKS

A factor in the burgeoning summer life of Antarctic seas is the number of links in the food chains. The rorqual's main food is the shrimplike krill. These creatures eat tiny planktonic plants by their own filter-feeding mechanism, which strains the tiny food from the water. On a far vaster scale, rorquals filter krill in the same way. So there are only three links in this food chain: phytoplankton > krill > rorqual. In any food chain, energy and nutrients are lost at each link as animals move, respire, and excrete, so longer chains are less effective. This simple chain is the secret to the process by which some of the tiniest plants are converted into the largest animals on Earth.

---

oceans. It sometimes comes inshore but usually stays in the open sea. Sei whales are more moderate, staying mainly in subtropical, temperate, and subarctic regions. They rarely venture into the far Arctic and Antarctic, or into the warmest tropical seas, except to breed. Bryde's whales are found only in temperate and tropical seas, where the water temperature stays above 68°F (20°C). The minke whales are found inshore and offshore, in all seas, and at all latitudes, from tropics to poles.

### MIGRATIONS

Humpback whales have well-defined migrations across the open seas, which are the longest of any rorqual (and almost any other mammal). Since their cruising speed is fairly slow, only 4.3–5 mph (7–8 km/h), they spend many weeks on the move. But at the end of the journey, they prefer either to feed or breed in relatively shallow coastal waters, compared to other rorquals. Their migrations to traditional calving or feeding grounds at a regular time each year are also relatively predictable. However, some humpbacks stay at the northerly or southerly feeding sites during the winter, while others remain in the breeding areas during summer.

Blue and fin whales follow the seasonal north-south pattern. Fins do not venture as far into the poles and tropics as other rorquals, especially blues, and younger fins tend to make even shorter migrations so that they remain in temperate seas.

The migrations of the sei and Bryde's whales are much less predictable. They wander to wherever food is abundant, depending on the prevailing conditions. ∎

## FOCUS ON

### ANTARCTICA

Antarctica is the great southernmost continent—a landmass covering the South Pole, which is itself covered by an ice cap and totally surrounded by ocean. The continent itself is almost barren, but the Southern Ocean surrounding Antarctica, which merges into the South Pacific, South Indian, and South Atlantic Oceans, is not. Two of the three conditions for life exist in abundance: light and nutrients. In the summer, the sun is high in the sky for eighteen hours or more daily. Nutrients are brought in and circulated by the Antarctic current, which is up to 1,250 miles (2,000 km) wide, flows around the continent at a speed of 12 miles (19 km) a day, and reaches depths of 7,540 ft (2,300 m). All this encourages plankton growth and one of the richest marine ecosystems on Earth, including baleen and toothed whales (especially the killer), seals, penguins, fish, squid, and mollusks in incredible numbers.

### DIVING SEQUENCE OF RORQUALS

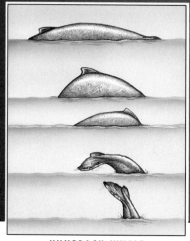

**HUMPBACK WHALE**

*A humpback makes high rolling dives. Its habit of raising the tail flukes high sets it apart from other rorquals.*

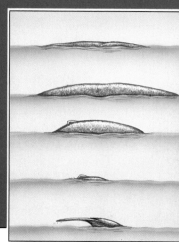

**BLUE WHALE**

*Although a veritable giant, the blue whale is sleek and graceful in the water. The tail flukes appear fleetingly.*

Diving illustrations Evi Antoniou

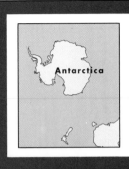

Carolyn Gohier/Ardea

**MIDSUMMER THAW**
*Only 2 to 3 percent of Antarctica's vast landmass is ever exposed by the melting of ice, and this occurs only in midsummer. In winter, the ice caps extend into the surrounding seas.*

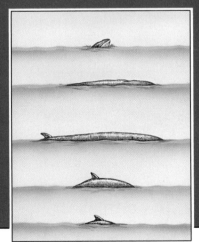

**SEI WHALE**

*Neither arching the back nor showing the tail flukes, the sei whale slips quietly underwater.*

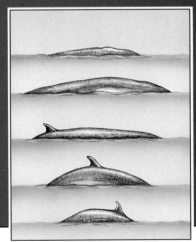

**BRYDE'S WHALE**

*Surfacing after a deep dive, Bryde's whale shows a long expanse of back before humping the tail stock.*

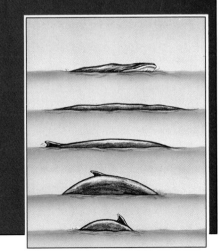

**FIN WHALE**

*The fin whale follows a similar diving pattern to the Bryde's whale. The larger fin is set farther back.*

# FOOD AND FEEDING

Jeff Foott Productions/Bruce Coleman Ltd.

*Several family groups of humpbacks may join together to form a larger band at feeding sites.*

closing its mouth, contracting the throat folds, and raising its tongue toward the roof of the mouth. It then uses its soft, fleshy tongue to lick the food that has been trapped on the inside of the baleen fringes.

### THE BALEEN
The key to rorqual filter-feeding is baleen, or whalebone. It is not true bone, but a horny, fibrous substance consisting mainly of keratin (the substance that makes up fingernails). Each baleen plate is shaped roughly like a tall upside-down triangle, the base rooted in the roof of the mouth. The inner edges fray into fine, stringy bristles, and these catch the food. The bristles wear away but, like fingernails, baleen continues to grow throughout life.

Rorquals feed mainly during their summer excursions into cold water. Like the right, bowhead, and other baleen whales, the rorquals are filter feeders, but they are unique in that they possess pleated and very elastic skin tissue that covers almost their entire underside. These expanding pleats enable the rorquals to take vast mouthfuls of water, a technique known as gulping, bringing the food within the comblike strainer of baleen. To strain the food after taking in vast amounts of water, the whale forces the water out by almost

## RORQUALS' FAVORITE FOODS

**Blue:** krill, especially in the Southern Hemisphere, and other crustaceans
**Fin:** krill, copepods, some schooling fish
**Sei:** mainly copepods also krill and other crustaceans
**Minke and humpback:** krill in Southern Hemisphere, schooling fish in the north
**Bryde's:** almost exclusively schooling fish

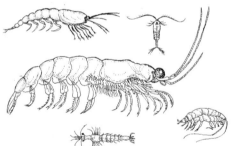

The baleen bristles have different textures and shapes in the different rorqual species, according to the preferred food.

### DIFFERENT TECHNIQUES

It is thought that rorquals probably find their food by smell and/or taste. The blowhole area has associated olfactory (smell) organs, and the front of the upper palette contains structures that are possibly smell-and-taste sensors. However, once food is located, the trapping techniques used tend to vary depending on the species. The most direct observations have been on the humpback (see panel).

Blue whales rarely dive deeper than 650 ft (200 m), even when there is more krill below. Fin whales sometimes turn over on their backs and approach the food swarm from beneath, curling their bodies around it as they come right-side up to trap and engulf the food. Minkes go right into the pack ice, pushing their pointed noses up through thin ice to make holes for breathing.

Of all the rorquals, the sei whale has the most finely meshed baleen fibers and, like the right whales, often employs the skimming method of feeding. Here the whale swims, with its mouth half open, through the swarms of tiny food organisms. When a mouthful of organisms has been filtered through the baleen plates, it closes its mouth and swallows. ∎

### FINS FEEDING

*Fin whales have medium-textured baleen bristles and eat mainly krill and copepods. Their elastic throat pleats expand to allow for the enormous quantities of water taken in when gulping.*

## HUMPBACK FEEDING METHODS

**The humpback uses a variety of feeding methods, the most fascinating being "bubble-netting." The humpback swims up from below in a helix, tracing a path like a corkscrew, with a school of krill in the middle. As it rises, the whale releases a steady stream of bubbles, which rise even faster. These form a cylindrical "wall" or bubble net around the krill, keeping them close together. The humpback then swims up inside the bubble net with its mouth open in the lunge-feeding manner. This involves swimming vertically toward the surface from deep water, the mouth partly open. Humpbacks cooperate to feed. Several individuals swim around a large school of krill, herding them into a concentrated mass. Individuals take turns lunging.**

Color illustration Mark Stewart/Wildlife Art Agency. B/W illustrations Ruth Grewcock

# SOCIAL STRUCTURE

Our knowledge of the social life of rorquals is largely guesswork. Toothed whales such as killers and belugas live in shallow waters near coasts and surface often, so observers can study them in more detail. But the great whales are not as amenable.

Blue whales are found in close-knit groups of three to four, forming larger groups for breeding. These rorquals may also gather in numbers at a rich food source, or perhaps to migrate as a group. The individuals, however, have little interaction.

Fin whales are slightly more sociable, occurring as individuals, pairs, and small bands of five to ten. In an area of concentrated food, there may be dozens of fins. However, they seem to take little notice of each other and will avoid close contact.

Seis live in groups or pods of three to six, which may be based on families. Pair bonds between male and female seis can last for several years.

---

**SOME OF THE PULSED SOUND EMITTED BY THE RAUCOUS RORQUALS MAY REPRESENT A PRIMITIVE SONAR**

---

Bryde's whale is another apparently unsociable rorqual, usually occurring alone, in male-female pairs, or mother-baby pairs. This is a fairly active great whale, like the humpback, and it sometimes breaches clear of the water.

Minke whales swim alone or in twos and threes. If more are sighted, they have usually congregated at a rich feeding site. These smallest rorquals are also

### SEI PODS

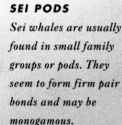

*Sei whales are usually found in small family groups or pods. They seem to form firm pair bonds and may be monogamous.*

the most inquisitive, sometimes approaching ships, which makes them suitable for whale-watching.

All of the rorquals make vocalizations, variously described as grunts, moans, thumps, buzzes, clicks, and hums. They are low in pitch (sometimes too low for our own ears) and carry well through hundreds of miles of water. The blue whale makes the loudest sounds of any animal, an incredible thunder-grunt estimated at 188 decibels. Their long moans last up to half a minute and are at very low frequencies.

### HUMPBACK SOCIETY

It is still unclear as to why the great whales sing, although most sounds do appear to be communicative, to do with courtship and perhaps territory. However, detailed studies of humpbacks—the most gregarious of the rorquals—being carried out in their wintering waters off Hawaii, are beginning to provide some answers about whale song and rorqual behavior in general.

Humpbacks live in family groups of three or four and communicate with other groups. Several groups may join into a band of twenty or more. Courtship involves many different types of behavior, some of it quite violent. The breach or leap from the water is spectacular but little understood. It

ANT/NHPA

# (in) S I G H T

## SONGS OF THE HUMPBACK

Humpback whales are record-breakers in many areas. They produce the longest and most complex sounds of almost any animal. They emit sequences of moans, groans, roars, sighs, high-pitched squeaks, and chirps, ranging widely in frequency. The sequences last for ten minutes or more and are repeated perfectly, over and over again. The beginning and end are often marked by click-ratchet and blowing noises. If a whale interrupts its song, it continues exactly where it left off.

A typical song is made up of sections called themes, which are further divided into phrases. The song is repeated for hours or days at a time, with the whale pausing only to surface and breathe. It seems that all the humpbacks in one area produce the same song at the same time. However, individuals each have their own voice characteristics, enabling scientists to identify them even though they are singing the same tune. Songs vary in different areas. There are three recognized humpback dialects: North Pacific, North Atlantic, and Tonga (Southern Hemisphere).

*The humpback* (left) *is the best known and most closely studied of all the baleen whales.*

may be to rid the skin of parasites, to view the surroundings, to signal aggression, to communicate some intention, or an "exclamation point" at the end of other behavior. Humpbacks also fin-wave, holding one flipper up in the air as they roll or leap.

On migration, humpback social behavior changes dramatically. At this time, males rarely sing, and if they do, they stop when they join a group; the members travel together for some hours, then split up. At the feeding sites, temporary aggregations form mainly around abundant krill swarms; only mothers and calves remain together. ■

Color illustrations Kim Thompson

# LIFE CYCLE

A s with other aspects of behavior, more is known about courtship and mating in humpbacks than in other rorquals.

Every year, each humpback returns to its habitual breeding ground. The males arrive first and begin singing. They hang in the water 65–165 ft (20–50 m) down in a characteristic pose with head angled down and huge flippers dangling and announce their presence by song. When a female arrives, the closest male is attracted to her, then other males come, too, and they struggle and jostle to lie next to her.

Gradually more females arrive. Rival males threaten each other by slapping the water with their flukes or flippers. They also rear up from the water, blow massive bubbles, and even lunge at competitors with their

**MATING**

*The pair of mating humpbacks come together upright in the water, belly to belly and flippers clasping the partner, with most of their heads above the surface.*

**STAYING CLOSE**

*By the time the mother and calf return to the summer feeding ground, the calf is weaned, but it may continue to swim close to its mother.*

## AMAZING FACTS

- The blue whale calf is the world's biggest animal baby, at 23 ft (7 m) long and up to 3.3 tons in weight.

- Even as it grows in the womb, it puts on 2.2 tons in the last two months of pregnancy.

- After birth this big baby suckles about 100 gallons (almost 400 liters) of high-fat, high-protein mother's milk every day and puts on 175 pounds per day—the weight of a fairly large man, and the greatest growth rate of any mammal.

- By seven months of age, when a human baby weighs some 17 lb (8 kg), the young blue whale weighs 2,000 times more and has reached 42 ft (13 m) in length.

Color illustrations Barry Croucher/Wildlife Art Agency

mouths or tail flukes, sometimes causing injuries.

Courtship in other rorquals seems to be much less sophisticated—or it has simply not yet been observed.

### BREEDING CYCLE

The breeding cycle of the rorquals is closely linked to their migratory habits. The general pattern is that calving usually takes place in the warmer waters of the subtropics. Females who gave birth in the previous year, and whose calves are now weaned and independent, mate around the same time. Since the gestation period is about eleven months in most species, calves are born on return to the wintering areas in the following year.

The mother rorqual gives birth, usually to a single calf, in the usual mammal way. The mother suckles her newborn, using her abdominal muscles

# GROWING UP

*The life of a young humpback*

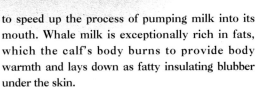

### GIVING BIRTH

*The mother rorqual gives birth, usually to a single calf. The calf emerges headfirst, and she may nudge it to the surface so that it can take its first breaths.*

### FEEDING

*As soon as the single calf is born, it fastens on to its mother's nipple (left), which protrudes from folds of skin on her underside, called the mammary slit.*

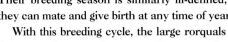

| FROM BIRTH TO DEATH | |
| --- | --- |
| **BLUE WHALE** | **HUMPBACK WHALE** |
| **GESTATION:** 11–12 MONTHS | **GESTATION:** 11–12 MONTHS |
| **NUMBER OF CALVES:** 1 | **NUMBER OF CALVES:** 1 |
| **LENGTH AT BIRTH:** 23 FT (7 M) | **LENGTH AT BIRTH:** 13–16 FT (4–5 M) |
| **WEIGHT AT BIRTH:** 5,500 LB (2,500 KG) | **WEIGHT AT BIRTH:** 2,800 LB (1,300 KG) |
| **SEXUAL MATURITY:** 6–12 YEARS | **SEXUAL MATURITY:** 5–10 YEARS |
| **LENGTH AT SEXUAL MATURITY:** 72–75 FT (22–23 M) | **LENGTH AT SEXUAL MATURITY:** 36–39 FT (11–12 M) |
| **LONGEVITY:** 65–75 YEARS | **LONGEVITY:** 70–80 YEARS |

have the regular migrations of other rorquals. Their breeding season is similarly ill-defined, and they can mate and give birth at any time of year.

With this breeding cycle, the large rorquals produce a calf every other year. However, there is evidence that some females are reproducing every year. They give birth, then mate shortly afterward. The reason may be that their numbers are lower since commercial whaling began, and so there is more food available and less competition for it.

### MATURING EARLY

Another effect of the low population, and greater food supplies, is that juveniles are reaching sexual maturity younger. Whales tend to mature at a certain body length, not at a set age; so if they can eat more and grow faster, they can breed younger. For example, it is estimated that in the past 50 years, the average age of sexual maturity in minke whales has fallen from 13–14 years to 6–7 years.

Both of these effects—breeding more frequently and at a younger age—may help the whale populations increase more rapidly. ∎

to speed up the process of pumping milk into its mouth. Whale milk is exceptionally rich in fats, which the calf's body burns to provide body warmth and lays down as fatty insulating blubber under the skin.

The mother protects her baby, who continues to feed for six months, while the pair return to their summer feeding ground. It is then weaned.

Bryde's whales feed for most of the year in their subtropical and tropical waters and do not

*A humpback and nursing calf. The mother and calf have a very close bond with one another.*

# LARGE MOVING TARGETS

**RORQUALS ARE IMPRESSIVE ANIMALS, YET DESPITE OUR AWARENESS OF THEIR HIGHLY ADVANCED BRAINS, SOME COUNTRIES SEEM BENT ON HUNTING THEM TO THE BRINK OF EXTINCTION.**

Whaling has occurred on a small and traditional scale for thousands of years. It began as far back as the 12th century, with fleets of sailing ships operating from western Europe. It wasn't until the 1700s that large-scale commercial whaling gained major momentum.

The rorquals' slow-swimming baleen cousins, the right whales, were the early victims. They swam slowly, often resting at the surface, and so were easy targets. However, the sleek, speedy rorquals could usually outrun ships under sail, and their great size meant they could escape from or shrug off the relative pinpricks of small harpoons.

As a result, a new harpoon gun with an explosive head, and a cannon gun to fire it, were invented in the 1860s. Faster boats were invented, too—first steamships, then turbine-driven screw ships.

### BIGGER AND BETTER WHALING

In 1906, large populations of whales were discovered in southern waters, and exploitation soon began there. Shore-based whaling stations had already been set up along the coasts of the Northern-Hemisphere whaling countries. As the whales were hunted to oblivion there, these stations fell into disuse. The whalers moved to the southern seas, and new processing stations were built on the closest available scrap of land. In other words, they simply began again. Remote and previously ignored islands such as South Georgia and the Kerguelens became busy with bubbling blubber vats, meat-packing halls, and bone-grinding machinery. It was a bad year for whales.

The large, modern-style whaling factory ship was developed in the 1920s. It had a ramp or stern slipway at the back to haul up carcasses. This made it independent of shore-based whaling stations. It was now possible to travel far out to sea,

where the blues and other rorquals swam. A fleet of attendant catcher boats located, chased, and harpooned the whales. Rorquals sink when dead, so whalers inflated their bodies with air pumped through lances to make them float.

The factory ship had the tryworks, refrigerators, processing machines, and other equipment needed to reduce an entire whale to usable products in one hour. On deck, the vast animals were rapidly flensed—the blubber and meat were stripped off with large blades on broomstick-sized handles. The products could be stored for the duration of the voyage, perhaps for many months, inside the refrigerators. Even the tube-shaped sheath of skin over the penis, some 6 ft long, was used. Whalers cut it off carefully and treated it to make rainproof capes.

As the numbers of whales continued to fall, whalers made faster boats and more effective

David Woodfall/NHPA

*Greenpeace has done much to highlight the plight of the whales. The SS* Sirius *awaits "orders" (above).*

Ken Balcomb/Bruce Coleman Ltd.

## THEN & NOW

*This map shows the numbers of rorqual populations (in thousands) both before exploitation and as they approximately stand today.*

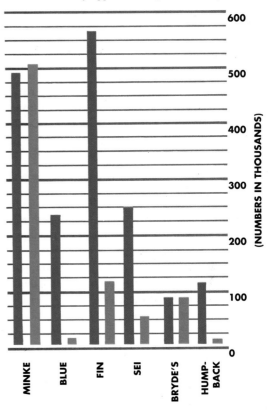

(NUMBERS IN THOUSANDS)

600
500
400
300
200
100
0

MINKE  BLUE  FIN  SEI  BRYDE'S  HUMP-BACK

■ BEFORE EXPLOITATION     ■ NOW

**These numbers are approximate. Rorquals are difficult to count because they roam over large areas and stay submerged for long periods. As a result, estimates of population sizes vary enormously. Some experts say that a large amount of double-counting is almost inevitable, and the true numbers of rorquals may be as low as half of those shown.**

harpoons. They also found better means to locate whales, including spotter planes, helicopters, and sonar. Many nations cashed in on the hunt, including the United States and Great Britain.

THE DECLINE OF THE HUMPBACK
The humpback whale was slow and conspicuous at the surface. It also seemed unaware of approaching vessels. As a result, mass exploitation of humpbacks began in the 19th century, and almost at

*A whaler and his quarry, a fin whale. Some countries continue whaling despite bans.*

ENDANGERED SPECIES

## (in)SIGHT

### STRANDING

**Compared to many other cetaceans, rorquals rarely strand. This is partly because they live in the open ocean, far from land. Those that do may well have died from sickness out at sea and gotten washed ashore by winds and currents. Live rorqual beachings are exceptionally rare. Out of thirty humpback whales that have stranded since the early 1980s, only one was reported alive. This stranding occurred on Cape Cod.**

once the populations in the North Atlantic and North Pacific virtually disappeared. Large stocks were then discovered in the Southern Hemisphere, and between 1900 and 1940, at least 100,000 humpbacks died. There was some hope around 1920 when catches were much reduced, but hunting was renewed in the 1930s and 1950s. Finally, legal protection was phased in between 1946 and 1966.

HOW THE RORQUALS SUFFERED

The blue whales, being the biggest, were the most profitable and so the prime quarry for whalers. As with other rorquals, most were taken from their summer cold-water feeding grounds, principally in

IN THE 1930S, AT THE HEIGHT OF THEIR SLAUGHTER, SOME 30,000 BLUE WHALES WERE KILLED EVERY YEAR

the Southern Hemisphere, when their well-fed carcasses yielded far more flesh and blubber.

The mass slaughter of blue whales gathered speed from the beginning of this century. It peaked in the 1930s. By the 1950s their numbers were so low that hunting them was no longer economical. The blue whale was finally protected by worldwide laws in 1966–67.

As the number of blue whales declined, the whalers turned to fin whales, with more than 30,000 being caught in some years during the 1950s and 1960s. Protection for fins in the southern oceans came in 1976, followed by protection for the northern populations.

Sei whales were usually less preferred, compared to blues, fins, and humpbacks. Nevertheless, they too endured mass slaughter, mainly in the 1960s. Within a few years the numbers of seis of the southern oceans had plummeted. This species

# THE BLUE WHALE

**In the southern oceans, the humpback was the first rorqual to feel the steel of the whalers' harpoons. When this giant was depleted, they turned on the blue.**

No one knows how many blue whales there were before commercial whaling began. Estimates have varied greatly, but in 1900, best guesstimates put numbers at about 8,000 in the Northern and 220,000 in the Southern Hemisphere.

Initially, blue whales were simply too fast, too far away, and just too huge to be slaughtered by the masses. But by the early 1920s, technology had caught up and the species was all but wiped out in the Northern Hemisphere. In the 1930–31 season alone, about one-eighth of all the blue whales in the world were killed.

By 1930, whaling nations had brought in guidelines for annual whale catches. But the codes were voluntary and there was no upper limit on individual species, so blues remained obvious targets. By 1939–40, reported blue whale kills had fallen to some 12,600—although not through want of trying—and by 1959–60, the official tally was a paltry 1,465.

The writing loomed large upon the wall. From 1960 the IWC tried to stop all killing of blue whales. But several member nations resisted, and some employed dubious delaying tactics. In the 1965–66 season, 613 were reportedly killed. Finally, in 1966, the blue whale achieved

## CONSERVATION MEASURES

● In 1969, a group of Canadian environmentalists founded Greenpeace. One target for direct nonviolent action was whaling.

● In 1970 the United States banned the import of whale products.

● In 1973 the first twenty-three nations signed the Convention on International Trade in Endangered Species (CITES). All

full legal protected status. It was estimated that, including whales born at this time, some 300,000 had been killed during the main whaling period—all within the lifetime of just one of these giants.

Attention shifted to surveys of the blue whale and hopeful signs of recovery. In the early 1980s, their populations were estimated at 10,000–12,000 in the south and 3,000 in the north. But the survey methods, especially the twin-ship observers technique, were questioned. At the 1989 meeting of the IWC, estimates had fallen to as few as 500 in the Southern Hemisphere.

More recent surveys support estimates that the blue whale population is in the hundreds, rather than many thousands. The gloomiest predictions are that their numbers are still falling. Some experts are afraid that the species is unlikely to recover.

## RORQUALS IN DANGER

THE INTERNATIONAL UNION FOR THE CONSERVATION OF NATURE (IUCN), OR THE WORLD CONSERVATION UNION, PRODUCES OFFICIAL LISTS OF THREATENED ANIMALS. IN THE IUCN's 1994 LISTINGS, THE WHALES ARE CATEGORIZED AS FOLLOWS:

| | |
|---|---|
| BLUE WHALE | ENDANGERED |
| SEI WHALE, FIN WHALE, HUMPBACK WHALE | VULNERABLE |
| BRYDE'S WHALE, MINKE WHALE | INSUFFICIENTLY KNOWN |

CITES IS THE CONVENTION ON INTERNATIONAL TRADE IN ENDANGERED SPECIES, OPENED FOR SIGNING IN 1974. ALL CETACEANS—WHALES, DOLPHINS, AND PORPOISES—ARE ON THE CITES LISTS, INCLUDING, OF COURSE, ALL SIX SPECIES OF RORQUALS. TRADE IN THEM OR THEIR PRODUCTS IS LEGAL ONLY WITH SPECIAL LICENSES AND PERMISSION.

Kim Taylor/Bruce Coleman Ltd.

THE GIGANTIC BLUE WHALE (*ABOVE*) HAS BEEN HUNTED TO THE BRINK OF EXTINCTION.

rorquals are on the protected lists.

● In 1986 the IWC established a worldwide moratorium on all commercial whaling.

● In 1994 the IWC set up the Southern Sanctuary around Antarctica, encompassing the summer feeding grounds of at least four-fifths of all remaining great whales. Here, rorquals are protected year-round.

was protected by law in 1979, except for a small population in the North Atlantic.

Bryde's whale was largely overlooked as quarry. Japan and the U.S.S.R. hunted this species in the North Pacific, and some were caught off southern Africa and southern South America. However, in the 1970s, just as the whalers were looking to Bryde's as the next target species, a move came to stop all commercial whaling. Overall, Bryde's has escaped.

Minkes were always considered too small to be worth killing; that is, until the other rorquals had all but disappeared. However, the 1986 International Whaling Commision (IWC) moratorium has helped save the species, even though some traditional minke catches are still permitted under IWC regulations.

### COUNTING THE COST

The damage done by commercial whaling was obvious from the very start. Species by species, area by area, whales disappeared. Their slow breeding rates allowed them no time to recover their numbers. As far back as 1911, the British Museum called for an investigation into whaling and its possible effect on the whale populations of the world.

Their fears were well founded. In the 1930s perhaps two-thirds of all the blue whales in the world had been killed. A few attempts were made to limit catches, but nothing happened until 1945. The International Council for Exploitation of the Sea revealed that certain whales were under threat and suggested protecting young whales.

# ALONGSIDE MAN

## WASTE NOT, WANT NOT!

Almost every scrap of the rorqual whale was used for something. A single large blue whale could yield 66 tons of meat, 33 tons of blubber, and 16 tons of bones.

Oil, from the fatty blubber, was burned in lamps and then used as a hydrogenation ingredient in margarines, soaps, oil paints, and lubricants. The glycerine components of the oil have been used to make nitroglycerine explosives.

Whale meat is still a delicacy in Japan and some countries of Southeast Asia. However, the trade is often illegal, and it is claimed that whale meat originating from Norway has been illegally sold to Japan and South Korea.

The springy, resilient bones of the baleen whale enjoyed a fashionable career as stays in whalebone corsets. Flexible stays today could, of course, be made from plastic. Whale cartilages and bones were made into glues or ground up for fertilizer. Almost any body part could be put into pet foods.

Scrimshaw is the art of carving or engraving on whalebone, whale teeth, and ivory. It began in the 1820s as a way of passing time on whaling ships. The sailors made many beautiful items such as jewelry boxes, ornaments, toys, and utensils.

The blue whale remains on the critical list. It may still be at grave risk of complete extinction. In any case, even if this is avoided, it may never return to its former numbers (see Endangered Species, pages 2338–2339).

### IS RECOVERY POSSIBLE?

There were reports in 1993 that humpback whales, protected since 1963, may be recovering. Australian researchers reported population increases in two groups that swim past the west and east coasts of Australia, on their way to warmer waters, to give birth. They may now number as many as 5,000. This figure was thought to be the number of all the humpbacks in the Southern Hemisphere. More recent estimates, which include the humpbacks off South Africa and South America, put the total number of these rorquals in the Southern Hemisphere as high as 10,000.

However, the populations are still a shadow of their prewhaling days. The humpbacks that travel past eastern Australia may once have numbered as high as 20,000. By the 1960s, they were down to 200. Now the number may be back to 2,000, having almost trebled in the past decade. ■

As a result, the International Whaling Commission was set up in 1946. It gradually introduced lists of protected species, closed areas of sea where whaling should not take place, and declared open and closed seasons for hunting.

In the 1950s and 1960s, people began to realize that whales were relatively intelligent animals, with mother-baby bonds and social lives. Whales felt pain and died in agony from the harpoons.

### SPEAKING OUT

People began to speak out against the killing. Save the Whale campaigns became popular as the World Wide Fund for Nature (WWF), Greenpeace, and Friends of the Earth took up interest. In the early 1970s, Greenpeace's policy of direct nonviolent action meant sailing their inflatable boats between the whaling ships and the whales, in the path of the harpoons. This resulted in invaluable publicity footage.

The United States banned the import of whale products in 1970 and commercial whaling in its waters in 1972. Many other nations took the same steps. This has been achieved partly through the CITES international trade agreement. Some countries joined the IWC simply to speak out against whaling (see Into the Future, page 2341).

*The slow and unwary humpback whale has paid a high price for its friendliness.*

François Gohier/Ardea

# INTO THE FUTURE

**S**afe at last? In April–May 1994, the International Whaling Commission (IWC) declared a vast ocean sanctuary around Antarctica in which all whaling, both scientific and commercial, would be prohibited. The boundary follows the 40°S latitude, except near Chile, where it dips to 60°S, and in part of the Indian Ocean, where it dips to 55°S, to take into account an existing sanctuary north of this line.

The Antarctic Ocean refuge is the main feeding area for about three-quarters of the world's remaining great whales. It is expected that all nations, including Japan, will respect the agreement, which will be reviewed every ten years.

However, there are still problems. Not all nations tell the truth about whales and whaling. Russia recently admitted that it secretly killed whales for years in defiance of laws and bans. In the Antarctic during the 1960s, their official figures for

## PREDICTION

### TOO LITTLE TOO LATE?

*The current hope is that all rorqual species will slowly recover some of their numbers. The blue and humpback populations are most devastated, and their return is still in the balance. It will take decades, even centuries. It is doubtful if they will ever return to their original size, since the food chains of the oceans may have been irreversibly altered.*

Antarctic kills were 156 blues and 152 humpbacks. Yet ships' logs show that just one of their four vessels killed over 1,400 blues and 7,000 humpbacks.

Japan, Norway, Iceland, and other nations with great-whaling traditions continue to press for the lifting of the IWC moratorium that was passed in 1982 to phase out all commercial whaling. They want an IWC Revised Management Plan to be adopted, which would allow for the resumption of small-scale commercial whaling, especially of minkes. They argue that this would not harm their populations and might be beneficial for other, larger rorquals, since it would leave more krill for them to eat.

Norway now faces sanctions as a result of having resumed commercial whaling for minkes in 1994, in defiance of the IWC moratorium. Iceland left the IWC in 1992 as a protest of the continuing moratorium. Although it still observes the moratorium, it threatens to resume commercial whaling. ■

## THE NEW ECOLOGY

Massive shifts in the ecology of the oceans, especially around Antarctica, may mean that the roquals will never regain their original numbers. As the blue and other great whales were slaughtered, the krill that they would have eaten has become available to other animals. It is estimated that this potential krill surplus is more than 110 million tons.

Other krill-eaters have not been slow to take advantage of the food boom. Penguins, squid, crabeater seals, and Antarctic fur seals have increased in numbers, along with flying seabirds and other seals. Also, humans have begun to harvest krill. Because of their vast numbers and nutritive qualities—they are an especially rich source of vitamin A—krill has been regarded by ecologists as a potential food source for humans.

Krill-eaters in general will not give up their newfound prosperity without a fight. So the blue whale, in particular, must battle against lack of food, as well as against less chance of finding a mate in the wide ocean, and all the other problems that come with being so scarce.

## WHALES ON SATELLITE

*The space age has reached the world's largest animal. In 1994 Oregon State and Cornell Universities began a project to attach electronic tags to blue whales in the eastern Pacific. These detect and record information such as water depth, pressure, and temperature; how long and how deep the whale dives; and how deep it is when it sings. As the whale surfaces to breathe, these data are transmitted in less than a second to a satellite, which also pinpoints the whale's position, and all the information is relayed back via a ground station to the project's headquarters. A previous, less-accurate system tracked one blue whale for forty-three days—it covered about 34 miles (55 km) each day.*

Illustration Steve Kingston

# SPERM WHALES

Toothed whales belong to the order Cetacea and the suborder Odontoceti. Members of this suborder are as follows:

**PORPOISES**

**DOLPHINS**

**RIVER DOLPHINS**

**SPERM WHALE**

**BEAKED WHALES**

T. Arnbom/Planet Earth Pictures

CLASSIFICATION

The sperm whales, beaked whales, and white whales are three families of toothed whales. Along with five other families, which include the dolphins and porpoises, they make up the toothed-whale group, the suborder Odontoceti. There is another whale suborder, the Mysticeti, which comprises the baleen, or whalebone, whales.

**ORDER**

Cetacea
(whales)

**SUBORDER**

Odontoceti
(toothed whales)

**SPERM WHALE FAMILY**

Physeteridae

**BEAKED WHALE FAMILY**

Ziphiidae

**WHITE WHALE FAMILY**

Monodontidae

# THE OCEAN'S GIANTS

**IN THE OPEN OCEANS LURKS THE BIGGEST, MOST POWERFUL MEAT-EATER EVER TO LIVE ON EARTH. THE GREAT SPERM WHALE IS TEN TIMES HEAVIER THAN EVEN THE DINOSAUR *TYRANNOSAURUS REX***

I t is dark and quiet in the deep ocean. Suddenly there is a noise like a bellowing, high-pitched siren. It is the burst of sound from a great sperm whale—so loud it literally stuns its prey into paralysis or death. The huge sperm whale is about to attack the biggest of all the invertebrates, or animals without backbones—a giant squid.

The battle rages. The sperm whale snaps at the slippery, squirming, 65-ft- (20-m-) long squid with its sharp teeth. The squid wraps its long tentacles around the whale and sticks its round suckers to its skin, trying to hold it down and block its blowhole, so that the air-breathing mammal drowns.

At last the squid tires and the whale bites into its brain and heart. Finally the great predator begins its meal, swallowing huge lumps of the squid's spineless flesh.

How do we know that this happens, in the blackness of the deep ocean? Because some sperm

*Blainville's beaked whale* (below) *swimming near the Hawaiian islands.*

James D. Watt/Planet Earth Pictures

whales have been caught and show deep, rounded scars on their skin, reasonably presumed to be made by the powerful suckers of the squid. Also, sperm whales have been killed and opened to reveal the remains of giant squid in their stomachs.

### TYPES OF TOOTHED WHALES

The sperm whale is the biggest member of the toothed-whale group. There are some 76 species of whales and dolphins in the world's oceans, forming the group Cetacea. Ten of these are baleen or whalebone whales, while the other 66 species are called odontocetes and belong to the toothed-whale subgroup, Odontoceti (o-don-to-SET-ee).

The Odontoceti are divided into six smaller groups, or families. Three of these, the dolphins, river dolphins, and porpoises, are described in Volume 5. The other three—sperm whales, beaked whales, and white whales—are included here.

The massive sperm whale can be identified by its great size; enormous head with its bulging, barrel-shaped forehead; slim, long, low-slung

---

**TOOTHED WHALES ARE TYPICALLY WHALE-SHAPED—ACTIVE HUNTERS WITH SHARP, CONE-SHAPED TEETH**

---

lower jaw; and a small lump where other whales have a proper dorsal (back) fin. It has two much-smaller cousins: the dwarf sperm whale and pygmy sperm whale. They are all deep-water whales.

The 18 species of beaked whales are mostly medium-sized—around 16–32 ft (5–10 m) long.

*A sperm whale* (right) *keeps a watchful eye over her recently born calf.*

Worldwide Fund for Nature/Bruce Coleman Ltd.

They are generally uncommon and seldom-sighted animals that live far out in the oceans and spend much of their time well underwater. Little is known about their habits and lifestyle, or even their bodily features, except for the few species that were popular with whalers. These included the northern and southern bottlenose whales, with their bulging foreheads, and Baird's beaked whale.

The beaked whales get their name from the peculiar beak-shaped mouth. This is made of the jutting-out upper and lower jaws that look similar to a dolphin's. Although beaked whales are included in the toothed-whale group, many of them have no teeth at all in the upper jaw. In fact, in most females, none of the teeth ever erupt, or grow up above the level of the gums, so these toothed whales appear toothless. The males of some species have two large teeth in the lower jaw that stick out beyond the lips, like a boar's tusks.

### CANARIES AND UNICORNS

There are two species of white whales, both about 16 ft (5 m) long. One is the all-white, or actually all-gray, beluga—often simply called the white whale. Many whales make underwater sounds for communicating, finding their way, and locating prey, but the beluga is probably the noisiest of all. Old-time sailors called it the sea canary.

The other white whale is the narwhal, or narwhale, with a whitish belly and dark mottled back. The male grows an extraordinary spiral-grooved tusk, which can reach 10 ft (3 m) in length. In

## MOBY DICK

*Moby Dick* is an adventure story written by Herman Melville and published in 1851. Moby Dick—the "great white whale"—was a huge, whitish, male sperm whale, recognizable by its color and the pattern of scars on its head and body. In a previous hunt, it bit off the leg of Captain Ahab, who becomes obsessed by it and pursues it across the perils of the cold, open seas. The story ends with a colossal three-day battle between man and whale.

Sperm whales that are pale creamy gray, instead of the usual dark gray, do sometimes occur in nature—as Herman Melville knew. As a young man, he had worked as a deckhand on whaling boats. His descriptions of the methods and dangers of whaling in the mid-19th century are both exciting and accurate.

olden times it was given the name of sea unicorn, and it is sometimes called the unicorn whale.

### PREHISTORIC BEGINNINGS

Among the earliest fossils of a whale is Pakicetus (pack-i-SET-us), known only from a preserved skull found in Pakistan. An air-breathing mammal about 6.5 ft (2 m) long, it was probably like a large otter.

Only 10 million years later, true whales swam in the oceans. Basilosaurus (bass-il-o-sore-rus) was over 65 ft (20 m) long and had a typical streamlined whale shape and sharp teeth. Its front limbs had evolved into flippers, while its rear limb bones were very small and hidden in its body. At its rear end there was probably a pair of flukes, like the flukes or "tail" of today's whales. (Flukes are not legs—they are filled with muscle and other flesh.) Like Pakicetus, it belonged to a group of whales called archaeocetes, (ark-AY-o-seats), which are all now extinct.

Just how whales evolved is not well known, mainly because of the lack of fossils. It seems that the toothed whales and baleen whales probably split from each other around 40–45 million years ago. The toothed whales may have been a side branch of the archaeocete group.

---

**WHALES ARE AIR-BREATHING MAMMALS THAT RETURNED TO THE SEA OVER FIFTY MILLION YEARS AGO**

---

One of the first toothed whales was Prosqualodon (pro-SQUALL-o-don) from about 30 million years ago, fossils of which have been discovered in South America, Australia, and New Zealand. It was around 8 ft (2.4 m) long and looked like a long-nosed, saw-toothed dolphin. Its breathing nostrils had moved from the snout tip to make a blowhole on the top of the forehead, as in whales today.

### ANCIENT AND MODERN

From the features of the skull bones and teeth, the beaked whales are among the most ancient of the living toothed whales (river dolphins may have an even longer history). The sperm whales may also have evolved in the Oligocene epoch, 35–38 million years ago. The white whales are probably cousins of the dolphins and porpoises and split from them some 10–15 million years ago.

Evolution can be suggested from genetics as well as fossils. Beaked and sperm whales are probably relatives because they have the same number of chromosomes, the microscopic X-shaped packages of genes—42 in each cell of the body. ■

# THE TOOTHED WHALES' FAMILY TREE

*There are two main kinds of whales—toothed whales, which include dolphins and porpoises, and baleen whales. Within the toothed-whale group, known as the Odontoceti, are six smaller groups: the dolphins, river dolphins, and porpoises; and the sperm, beaked, and white whales. Just how closely the various cetacean families are related to each other is not known for certain.*

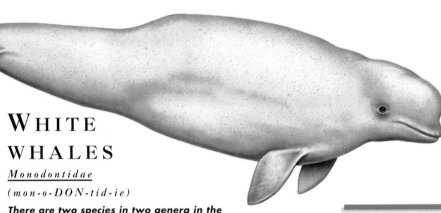

## WHITE WHALES

*Monodontidae*

*(mon-o-DON-tid-ie)*

**There are two species in two genera in the Monodontidae family, but they look very different. The beluga, or white whale, is very light in color as its alternative common name would suggest. The other species, the narwhal, has a long tusk and is often called the unicorn whale.**

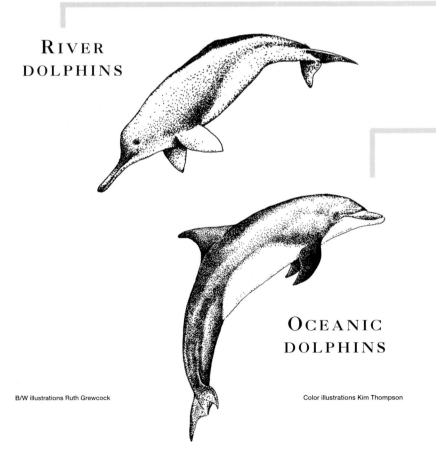

## RIVER DOLPHINS

## OCEANIC DOLPHINS

B/W illustrations Ruth Grewcock          Color illustrations Kim Thompson

# BEAKED WHALES

*Ziphiidae*
*(zi-FEE-id-ie)*

**There are eighteen species grouped in five genera. They are among the most primitive of the cetaceans. They are so elusive that one species, Longman's beaked whale, has never been seen alive. Evidence of its presence has come only from two skulls, one found in Australia and the other in Somalia, east Africa.**

# SPERM WHALES

*Physeteridae* *(FIE-set-er-id-ie)*

**This family contains three species in two genera and includes the largest toothed whale in the world—the sperm whale—characterized by an enormous rectangular head. It has the biggest gullet of any cetacean. Widely distributed, it is found in all oceans and adjoining seas of the world, although it is absent from polar ice fields.**

## PORPOISES

## TOOTHED WHALES

## BALEEN WHALES

## ALL WHALES

# ANATOMY:
## THE SPERM WHALE

The male sperm whale may weigh as much as 1,800 ten-year-old children! It grows to a maximum of 65 ft (20 m), the equivalent of six cars placed end to end. The dwarf sperm whale (top) is only 8 ft (2.5 m) long and weighs 440–550 lbs (200–250 kg). Yet even this is one-and-a-half times longer and three times heavier than an adult human.

### BRAIN

The sperm whale has the largest brain of any animal. The size and shape of a basketball, it weighs over 15 lb (7 kg). However, this is far smaller compared to its body size (0.02 percent) than a human brain compared to human body size (2 percent).

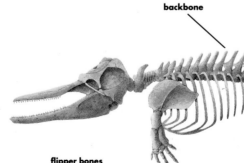

Illustrations Simon Turvey/Wildlife Art Agency

### BLOWHOLE

The sperm whale's S-shaped blowhole (breathing nostril) is at the front left tip of the forehead, which is a unique position among whales. When it blows after a dive, the spout of spray emerges to the whale's left at an unmistakable 45-degree angle.

### SKIN SCARS

The skin is smooth and hairless, as in most whales. The pale ridges and crescents of scar tissue that usually crisscross the head of old males are the result of fights with giant squid and other animals.

### EYE

Relatively small compared with body size, the eye cannot swivel in its socket, so the whale can only see to the side. Eyesight is limited to the surface waters, down to about 650–1,000 ft (200–300 m). Below this it is too dark to see.

**X-RAY**

The bones of a whale are light and spongy because they do not have to support the animal's weight—the water does this. Their main function is as an anchor for muscles. The sperm whale's rear limbs have disappeared during evolution. There are not even tiny remnants like those found in the baleen (whalebone) whales.

backbone

The flippers are equivalent to human arm bones but much shorter and broader. They are used for gentle rowing and paddling but mainly for steering. Most propulsive power comes from the tail flukes.

**SPERM WHALE SKELETON**

flipper bones

tail

X-ray illustrations Elisabeth Smith

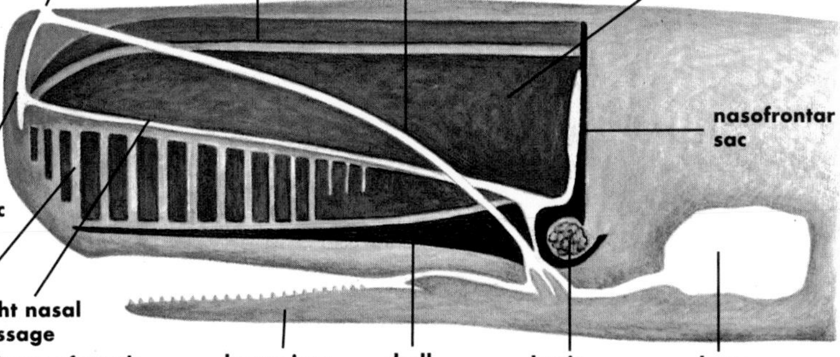

Labels on the head diagram:

blowhole · maxillonasalis muscle · left nasal passage · case · nasofrontar sac · vestibular sac · right nasal passage · spermaceti tissue of trunk · lower jaw · skull · brain · lung

## THE HEAD SHOWING SPERMACETI ORGAN

*The huge, squared-off, barrel-shaped forehead mainly houses the spermaceti organ. This is a tough, fibrous sheath, encased by muscle and blubber, which contains up to 2.9 tons (3 tonnes) of spermaceti—a milky-white, waxy liquid. It is probably a buoyancy and pressure adjuster for deep diving. On breathing, air passes from the blowhole, along the nasal passages, which go through the spermaceti organ, down and back to the whale's windpipe and lungs.*

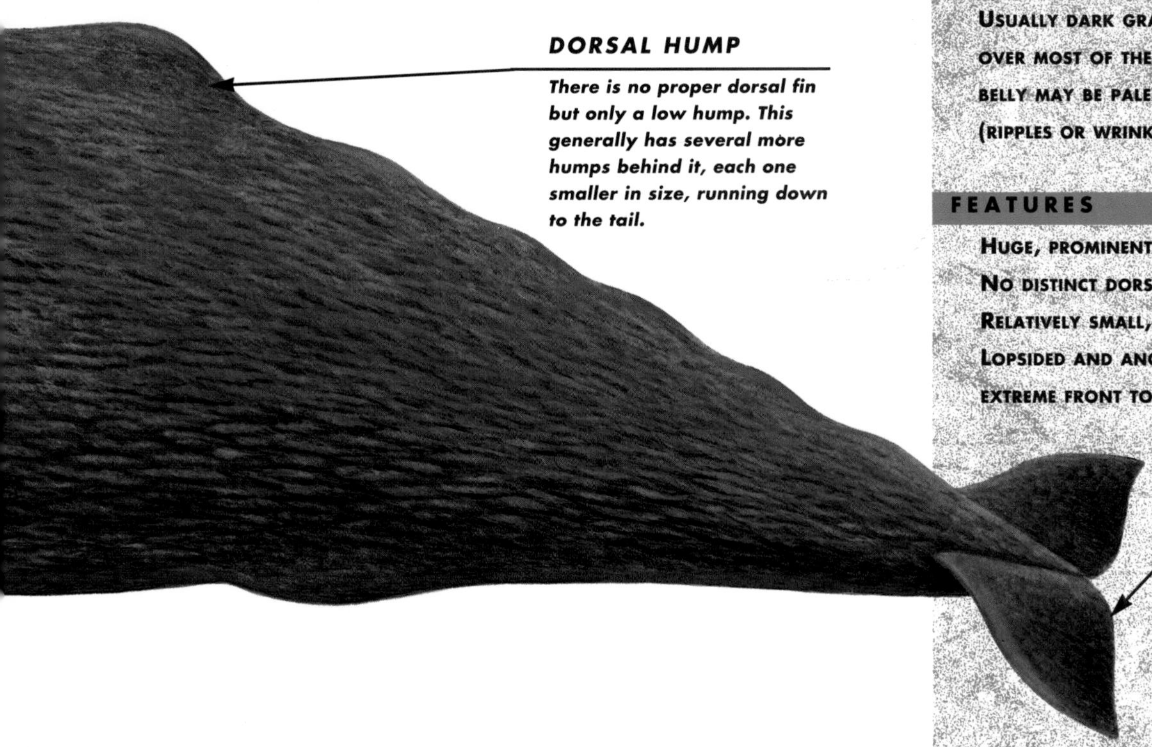

### DORSAL HUMP

*There is no proper dorsal fin but only a low hump. This generally has several more humps behind it, each one smaller in size, running down to the tail.*

### CLASSIFICATION

**GENUS: *PHYSETER***
**SPECIES: *CATODON***

### SIZE

**TOTAL LENGTH/MALE:** AVERAGE 49 FT (15 M); HEAD IS ONE-QUARTER TO ONE-THIRD TOTAL LENGTH
**WEIGHT/MALE:** AVERAGE 33–43 TONS (30–40 TONNES)
**SIZE AT BIRTH:** 9.8–13 FT (3–4 M) LONG; 440–660 LB (200–300 KG) IN WEIGHT
THE SPERM WHALE IS ONE OF THE MOST SEXUALLY DIMORPHIC OF WHALE SPECIES—THAT IS, THERE IS A GREAT DIFFERENCE BETWEEN THE SEXES. FEMALES (COWS) ARE ABOUT ONE-HALF TO TWO-THIRDS THE SIZE OF MALES (BULLS)

### COLORATION

USUALLY DARK GRAY, BLUE-GRAY OR BROWN-GRAY OVER MOST OF THE BODY. THE LIPS AND MIDDLE BELLY MAY BE PALER. THERE ARE CORRUGATIONS (RIPPLES OR WRINKLES) ALONG THE BODY

### FEATURES

HUGE, PROMINENT, BLUNT, SQUARED-OFF HEAD
NO DISTINCT DORSAL FIN
RELATIVELY SMALL, LONG, THIN LOWER JAW
LOPSIDED AND ANGLED BLOWHOLE, ON THE EXTREME FRONT TOP OF HEAD, ON THE LEFT SIDE

### TAIL FLUKES

*These are wide, roughly triangular, and extremely powerful. They have the central rear notch, characteristic of many other whales.*

---

**SPERM WHALE SKULL LOCATION**

*The skull occupies only a small portion of the lower rear head, as the position of the eye shows. Most of the head is the spermaceti organ (see above).*

**SPERM WHALE UPPER JAW**

*About ten to twenty small teeth grow in the upper jaw, but in many sperm whales they never get large enough to show above the gum surface. There are also sockets in the upper jaw, into which the teeth of the lower jaw fit.*

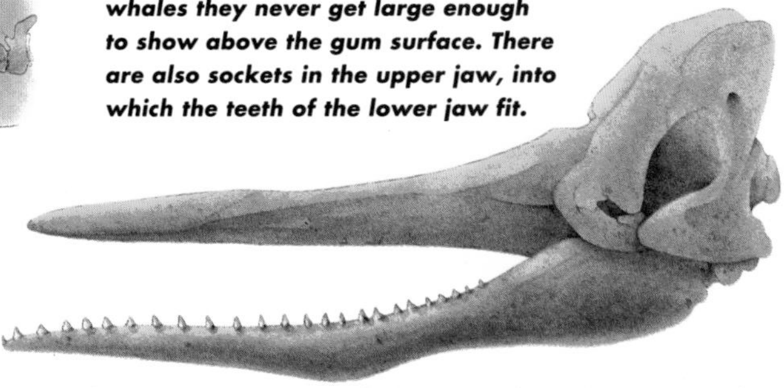

**SPERM WHALE LOWER JAW AND TEETH**

*The lower mandible (jaw) is slim and almost cylindrical for much of its length. The lower jaw does not reach the end of the head. On each side is a row of twenty to twenty-five teeth, which are rounded, cone-shaped, and fairly blunt. They fit into sockets in the upper jaw.*

# SOCIABLE NOMADS

## SPERM WHALES AND OTHER TOOTHED WHALES LIVE A WANDERING LIFE, ENDLESSLY MOVING AND MIGRATING THROUGH THE OCEANS. BUT BECAUSE THEY LIVE IN GROUPS THEY ARE FAR FROM LONELY

Toothed whales are generally social animals. They live in various kinds of groups, from mother-and-baby gatherings to herds of young males. The main exceptions are the adult male sperm whales, which live mostly on their own.

Much of our knowledge of whale behavior has come from the observations, anecdotes, and written records of the old-time whalers, as well as from tagging and radio-tracking of individuals, and from thousands of hours of patient observation in boats and aircraft. It is difficult for divers to observe whales directly unless the animals are near the surface and the weather is sunny and calm.

However, there are other clues to their habits, such as the makeup of groups that become stranded on land. Also, many male whales have been found with tooth-marks on the skin that correspond to the teeth of other males in their species. They acquire these from battling with one another for the right to mate with a particular female.

In order to keep in touch in the dark depths of the oceans, whales rely more on sound than sight. The different species make a variety of clicks, trills, squeaks, cracks, hisses, and roars, each of which seems to have a different meaning. Sounds travel over four times faster through water than through air, and a loud call can echo for a considerable distance through the sea.

These sounds also bounce off surfaces and objects nearby, allowing a whale to detect the echoes and analyze their patterns. It is a form of sonar, and it enables a whale to identify food items, friends and enemies, and the contours of the seabed for navigation.

Whales must come up to the water's surface regularly to breathe, and they often stay there as they rest. The light is brighter here and the whales can see each other. So sight is important, too.

One of the most exciting sights at sea is a fountain of spray jetting high into the air—the blow of a whale. This is the whale breathing out. The spray

*Living in the North Atlantic, these northern bottlenose whales* (above) *are taking a breather.*

*Beluga whales* (right) *congregate by the hundreds at their Canadian breeding grounds.*

Godfrey Merlen/Oxford Scientific Films

*The eye of a baby sperm whale* (below). *For its size, the eyes are small—it will rely more on hearing.*

Doug Perrine/Planet Earth Pictures

Tony Martin/Oxford Scientific Films

comes from its blowhole (nostrils) as it surfaces and is particularly powerful after a long dive. Whalers became experts at spotting and identifying blows, so they would know whether to give chase.

The blow is a mixture of stale, warm air from the lungs—which condenses into water vapor as it comes out into the cold—plus sprayed water that leaks though the blowhole during the dive, plus an aerosol of oils and mucus from the linings of the whale's lungs and breathing tubes.

A whale's blow is generally related to body size, although in the beaked whales it is relatively small—only 3 ft (1 m) high in the bottlenose whales. In belugas, the blow is so weak it is seldom seen.

Groups of whales may all surface and blow at

THE SPERM WHALE'S UNIQUE BLOW IS ONE OF THE MOST IMPRESSIVE OF ALL, REACHING UP TO 23 FT (7 M) HIGH

the same time. Narwhals come back up from their feeding dives, blow and breathe several times over a minute or so, and then take a final breath before descending again for another 20-minute dive. This coordination is achieved by sounds.

Traveling sperm whales swim in a loose group with members up to 330 ft (100 m) apart and communicate using sounds. The whales emit clicks at the rate of 30–60 each second. Leaving the whale's head, the clicks pass through its spermaceti organ. Each whale produces its own pitch of clicks and has a different shape of spermaceti organ, according to its sex and body proportions. So the organ gives a unique "sonic fingerprint," or "voice," to its clicks, by which other whales can recognize it. ∎

# HABITATS

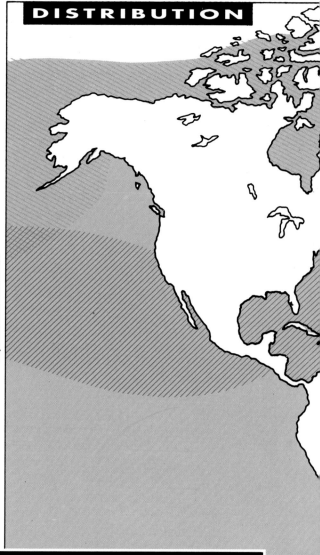

B elow the surface, oceans are as varied as the land. Currents are like winds, pushing water from place to place. Temperatures vary, getting cooler from equator to pole and from surface to seabed, and also being altered by currents. The seabed has flat plains, high mountains, jagged cliffs, and deep ravines.

This means that there are many different marine habitats. Like land creatures, each type of whale is adapted to one or more of these, but their distribution pattern is complicated by the fact that many species migrate during the year.

Great sperm whales are usually found far from land, or near oceanic islands where the sea floor plunges steeply into a deep trench. Females and youngsters tend to stay in warmer waters around

*Belugas arriving at an estuary after a migration of about 186 mi (300 km). It is in these warmer coastal waters that young from the previous year's mating are born.*

---

IT WAS ONCE THOUGHT THAT THE
NARWHAL USED ITS LONG TUSK TO MAKE A
BREATHING HOLE IN THE ICE

---

the equator and temperate regions, where the surface temperature is 60°F (15°C) or above. Adult males may venture to the cold poles in summer.

The pygmy sperm and dwarf sperm whales prefer the warmer temperate and tropical waters all around the globe. They tend to stay closer to land, over regions of continental shelf, where the depths are less than 820 ft (250 m).

Narwhals have been seen all around the Arctic Circle, but they are less common in the waters around eastern Asia, Alaska, and western Canada. They swim near the coast or along the edge of the pack ice and ice floes. Belugas also live in cold northern waters. They tend to stay in shallower waters even closer to the coast or the edge of the ice.

## THE MOST NORTHERLY WHALE

**Narwhals live in colder, more northerly waters than any other whale. They even venture into patches of clear water among the pack ice, swimming below the floating, frozen-in lumps and floes. If the small area of open water freezes over and they cannot reach a patch of ice-free sea to surface and breathe, they will drown. Narwhals tend to congregate and surface regularly—the resulting splashing of water helps to keep it from freezing. Their extra-strong skin and blubber insulate them from the intense cold.**

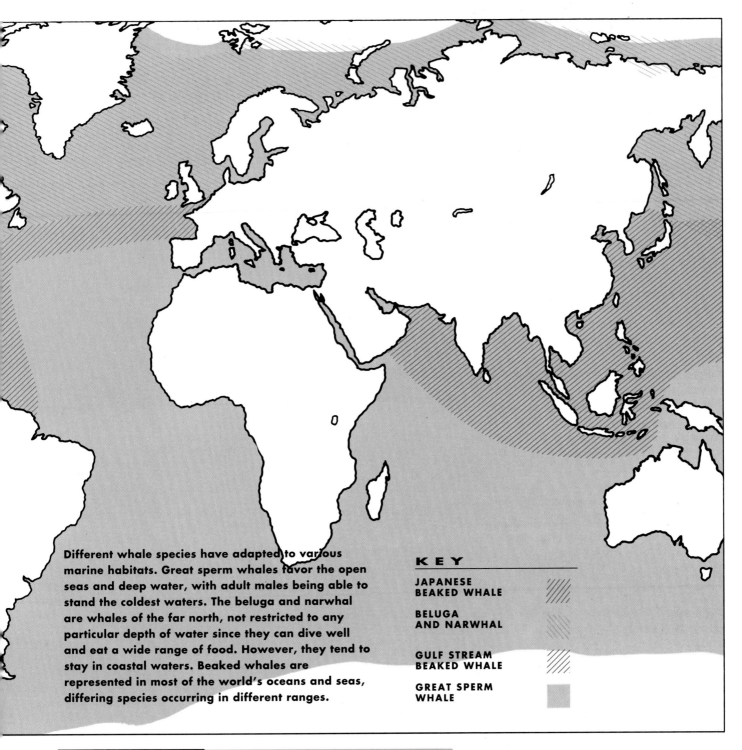

Different whale species have adapted to various marine habitats. Great sperm whales favor the open seas and deep water, with adult males being able to stand the coldest waters. The beluga and narwhal are whales of the far north, not restricted to any particular depth of water since they can dive well and eat a wide range of food. However, they tend to stay in coastal waters. Beaked whales are represented in most of the world's oceans and seas, differing species occurring in different ranges.

**KEY**

JAPANESE
BEAKED WHALE

BELUGA
AND NARWHAL

GULF STREAM
BEAKED WHALE

GREAT SPERM
WHALE

## KEY FACTS

● Most catchings and sightings of northern bottlenose whales have been in water deeper than 3,300 ft (1,000 m) and between 28°F to 63°F (-2°C to 17°C).

● Sighted off southern South America, southern Africa, and the southern third of Australia, the southern bottlenose rarely strays into water less than 820 ft (250 m) deep.

● Patches of clear water among the pack ice are called *savssats* in Inuit. It is here that the beluga loves to swim, often swimming underneath the ice floes.

Northern bottlenose whales range across the North Atlantic, occasionally coming as far south as the New England states or Portugal in Europe.

The southern bottlenose whale has a similar habitat in the Southern Hemisphere, although it extends across the South Pacific as well as the South Atlantic.

Cuvier's beaked whale is one of the most wide-ranging of all whales. It has been caught and observed in tropical and temperate seas all around the world. In contrast, Gervais' beaked whale is restricted to the western Atlantic Ocean, with sightings and strandings from New York down to the Caribbean. A few strays have reached West Africa and Ascension Island in the South Atlantic. ■

# MIGRATION

Migrations—mass long-distance journeys, often with a seasonal pattern—are less well understood in the toothed whales than in the large baleen whales. The sperm whale itself is fairly well studied, although its movements are complicated and depend partly on the makeup of the social group involved. The migrations of belugas are also well documented.

The information for other whale types is scanty, and the accepted views are partly guesswork. Lines of evidence include the frequency of strandings in different seasons. Whales may strand because they have strayed into an unfamiliar area, or dead whales may drift for days before being beached.

In the polar summers, long daylight hours combine with upwellings of nutrients brought by currents to feed trillions of tons of tiny floating plants and animals—the plankton that is the basis of many marine food chains. During the winter, however, polar waters are inhospitably dark and intensely cold, so the whales retreat to the warmer temperate and tropical seas. Many species take

---

**THE MAIN REASON WHY WHALES MIGRATE IS TO TAKE ADVANTAGE OF SEASONAL FOOD SUPPLIES**

---

advantage of the placid conditions closer to the equator to give birth and raise their young.

Nursery groups of sperm whales, consisting mainly of mothers and babies, swim to temperate waters for the summer and back to the tropics for winter. Bachelor herds of young males can travel faster and go farther north and south. The huge adult males swim alone and faster still and can reach Arctic and Antarctic waters for the polar summer. An individual may travel more than 6,200 mi (10,000 km) on its spring and autumn migrations.

The migrations of the dwarf sperm whale may follow the same pattern, toward temperate waters in summer and back to the Tropics in winter.

In the far north, both belugas and narwhals tend to stay near coasts or the edges of the floating pack ice. As the sea freezes in winter and the ice spreads southward, the whales are pushed south,

*Mean temperature of ocean waters for the warmest (right) and coldest (far right) months of the year in the Northern Hemisphere. The charts work in reverse for the Southern Hemisphere.*

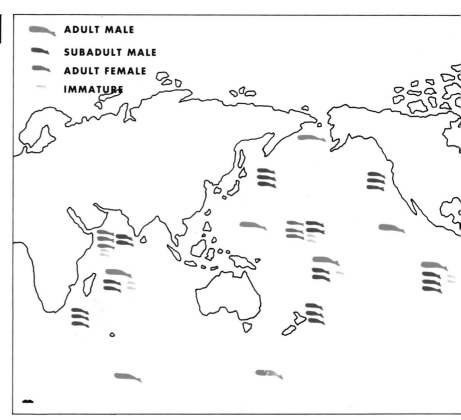

ADULT MALE
SUBADULT MALE
ADULT FEMALE
IMMATURE

**DISTRIBUTION MAP**
(above) *of sperm whales and their social groupings.*

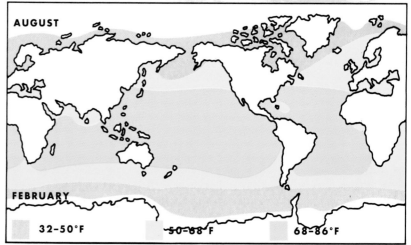

AUGUST

FEBRUARY

32–50°F     50–68°F     68–86°F

## STRANDED BEAKED WHALE

As soon as a whale is beached and loses the buoyant support of the water, its ribs cannot support the weight of its body. They collapse, squeeze the lungs, and prevent breathing, causing suffocation. Some beached whales are already injured, sick, or old, yet apparently healthy whales also "live-beach." Theories to explain this suggest confusion of the sonar system caused by shifting sandbanks, noise pollution from boat engines and propellers, heavy chemical pollution, effects of radio signals, or disruption from storms or underwater earthquakes. But statistical analyses to link such factors with live-beachings do not give clear results.

Illustrations John Morris/Wildlife Art Agency

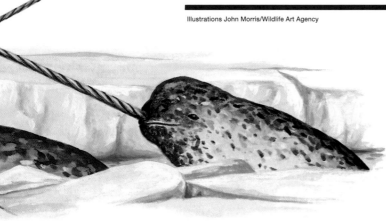

### NARWHAL

*Males often use their tusks in contests with each other to establish hierarchy.*

too. The spring thaw sees them moving back up to the northern areas. So the migrations are forced upon the animals by the advance and retreat of the ice. Should they become trapped under the ice, they would run out of air and drown.

Belugas tend to hang around bays and estuaries in summer, where the shallow, sheltered water warms up more quickly. They regularly swim up

THE MIGRATORY PATTERNS OF
MOST BEAKED WHALES IS LITTLE
KNOWN OR UNDERSTOOD

major rivers such as the St. Lawrence. They also tend to gather in larger groups than most other toothed whales. Smaller groups may come together as they swim on their journeys, until their mass migratory movements consist of thousands of individuals spread over several miles. ■

*Sperm whales move to the Arctic or Antarctic in the polar regions' warmest months of the year to take advantage of the flourishing food supplies.*

FEBRUARY

AUGUST

| 32–50°F | 50–68°F | 68–86°F |

# FOOD AND FEEDING

Toothed whales are all hunting creatures that live on a diet of other animals. Because they are bigger than most other sea creatures, they have their choice of a variety of food. However, the staple foods of most toothed whales are squid and fish.

Squid beaks are hard and tough and resist digestion, making them useful clues when examining the semidigested mush in a whale's stomach to see what it has eaten. Most of the swallowed flesh becomes soupy, but the beaks remain intact for many hours.

### SQUID SPECIALISTS

Most beaked whales are squid-eaters. Their strange tooth layouts—or rather, lack of teeth—pose no hindrance. The whales probably use their powerful mouth and neck muscles to suck in food.

The bottlenose whales, in particular, specialize in squid. The northern bottlenose whale is especially fond of the squid species *Gonatus fabricii*, and its range and migratory patterns strongly affect the whale's distribution. The stomach contents of the bottlenose have been known to contain deep-sea starfish, shrimp, sea cucumbers, and various fish.

White whales have a much more varied diet. Belugas forage on or near the bottom for capelin, char, cod, and similar schooling fish, as well as crabs and shrimp, clams, and seabed worms. They grab and crunch their prey with their sturdy, peg-shaped teeth. Belugas can also purse their fleshy, flexible lips to suck in small prey, or blow away mud to reveal victims. Groups of belugas have been seen to cooperate and "herd" a school of fish, trapping them against a rock or sloping beach.

Narwhals take mainly fish such as cod, flounder, and halibut, as well as the inevitable squid,

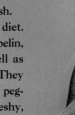

## in SIGHT

### "SIGHT" BY SOUND

In the dark ocean, eyes are not much use. Toothed whales have evolved an echolocation system to find their way and their food. The whale emits sounds of carefully controlled pitch and duration. These spread through the water and bounce off nearby objects as echoes. Toothed whales have forsaken their outer ear flaps for streamlining; only a small hole remains behind the eye. The inner parts of the ear are still present and work like those of other mammals.

Illustration Steve Kingston

Fred Whitehead/Oxford Scientific Films

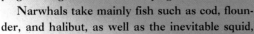
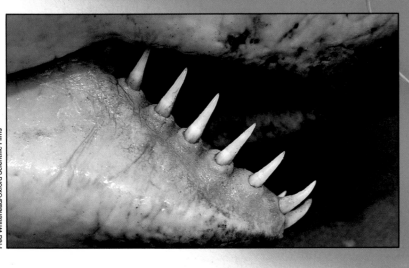

*Close-up of the teeth of the pygmy sperm whale —one of the stealthier hunters that creeps up and surprises its prey.*

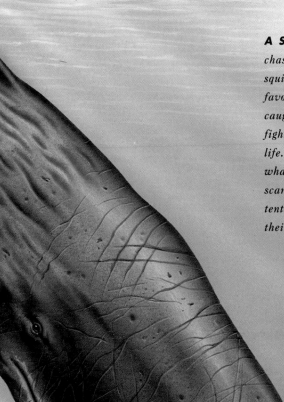

**A SPERM WHALE**

*chasing a giant squid, one of its favorite meals. Once caught, the squid fights bravely for its life. Many sperm whales bear the battle scars caused by squid tentacles cutting into their flesh.*

and also shrimp and other crustaceans. Male narwhals may stir up the seabed mud with their tusks to expose prey items, but tusks are obviously not essential for feeding, since females and young lack them. Sucking is probably their method of food capture, too, since they have no proper working teeth.

The sperm whale has an enormous food intake, as befits an enormous creature. About four-fifths of its food consists of squid, usually no more than about 3 ft (1 m) long. But some sperm

> IN ONE DIVE A SPERM WHALE CAN
> EAT THE EQUIVALENT OF
> FIVE WHOLE ADULT HUMANS

whale stomachs have contained giant squid 40 ft (12 m) long—swallowed whole. Other items in the sperm whale's diet include shrimp, crabs and other crustaceans, octopuses, and also such fish as lantern fish, certain cod species, redfish, and sharks and rays.

Pygmy sperm whales are stealthy hunters, creeping up on prey of squid and their molluscan cousins, the cuttlefish. They also ambush various fish, shrimp, and crabs. Dwarf sperm whales eat similar food, but the prey are correspondingly smaller, for the smaller mouth of the whale. ∎

## DEPTH CHART

| KEY | 6.2 mph | sea level |
|---|---|---|
| | 5.6 | |
| DESCENT SPEED | 5.0 | 3,300 ft |
| ASCENT SPEED | 4.3 | |
| DEPTH OF DIVE | 3.7 | 6,600 ft |
| | 3.1 | |
| *Depth chart of the great sperm whale showing the dive depth and speed of ascent and descent.* | 2.5 | 9,900 ft |
| | 1.9 | |
| | 1.2 | 13,200 ft |
| | 0.6 | |
| | 0 | 16,500 ft |

**FOOD**

CUTTLEFISH

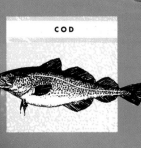
COD

LOBSTER

LONG-NOSED SKATE

NAUTILUS

Illustrations Ruth Grewcott

# BREACHING AND DIVING

**W**hales sometimes swim up from the depths very fast, propelling themselves right out of the water. For a second they seem to pivot like weighty ballerinas before they crash back onto the surface with an enormous splash. This is called breaching. Toothed whales indulge in this practice occasionally, but neither as often nor as spectacularly as the baleen whales—the humpback whale in particular.

The reason for breaching may be to get rid of itchy skin parasites or to send out a sound signal, or it may be simply for the fun of it. The true reasons are not fully understood.

One beaked whale that has been seen to leave the water completely during a breach is Cuvier's beaked whale. Together with the sperm whale, it has the habit of lifting its tail flukes clear of the water, almost vertically, as it begins to dive.

If not the champions at breaching, great sperm whales and beaked whales are undoubtedly the greatest divers of the whale world. Both species

**SPERM WHALES**

*often dive together, then fan out (above), making high-pitched clicks to keep in touch.*

**DIVE SEQUENCE**

*The four stages of the sperm whale's dive (below).*

---

**T**HE GREAT SPERM WHALE IS THE CHAMPION DIVER OF ALL, CAPABLE OF DESCENDING TO 10,000 FT (3,000 M)

---

can stay underwater for almost two hours and can reach depths of more than 3,300 ft (1,000 m). The sperm whale is the champion deep-diver. It has been tracked by monitoring its echolocation clicks down to 8,200 ft (2,500 m). One sperm whale caught and opened by whalers had eaten a species of seabed-dwelling shark. The nearest seabed in the vicinity at the time was over 10,000 ft (3,000 m) below where it was caught.

The sperm whale's incredible diving ability may be explained partly by the massive spermaceti organ in its head. The same oily substance it contains is present in most other whales and is believed to assist diving, but only in the sperm whale is it so abundant. As the whale dives, water pressure goes up and water temperature goes down. The whale's head cools from its normal 91.4°F (33°C), helped by the cold water let through the blowhole into the nasal passages. Below 84.2°F (29°C), the oil-like spermaceti turns thicker, more waxy and solid. It also contracts and becomes denser, or heavier. The effect

# *in* SIGHT

## SOCIAL STRUCTURE

**THE TAIL**

*of a sperm whale may be lifted almost vertically out of the water at the end of its dive.*

**Almost all species of sperm, beaked, and white whales are social creatures. They live in groups with others of their own kind, communicating regularly by various sounds and maintaining contact by sight in the lighter surface waters. Groups have different numbers and makeups of individuals, by age and sex, according to the species and season. Only rarely do toothed whales live alone.**

**The basic group of sperm whales is the nursery pod of 10–30 animals. The pod is led by the oldest female, the matriarch. During migration various pods unite in loose groups that can number over 1,000.**

**Beluga pods average 15 animals made up of all males of similar age, or females and young. Dwarf and pygmy sperm whales travel in smaller pods.**

of this makes the whale's head heavier, thereby reducing its buoyancy, and so making it easier for the whale to descend through the water.

As the creature rises, the changes are reversed. As the whale becomes more buoyant, it is able to float at the surface as normal.

### WHALES IN DISTRESS

If a sperm whale is in distress, it calls out with sounds loud enough to be heard a considerable distance away—in the air as well as in the water. (This is a factor that can also lead to mass strandings when several whales beach together.) Other members of the pod approach and try to help and support the caller. The whales circle around their distressed companion, and from above, their "daisylike" formation resembles the petals of a flower.

In the days of whaling, when one of the pod was harpooned, this helpful behavior turned to disaster for the whales. The whalers simply waited for the others to come near, and then shot them, too. Often 20 or more sperm whales would be picked off before the sea became so full of swirling cascades of blood and the screams of dying whales that the rest of the pod fled in panic. ∎

## BELUGA WHALE FACIAL EXPRESSIONS

The beluga has a fleshy, muscular mouth and lips. It is one of the few whales with a proper "neck," enabling it to move its head in relation to its body. Belugas are thought to use facial expressions to convey moods and intentions. By opening and closing the jaws and pursing or widening the lips, they seem to smile, kiss, grin—even frown. However, this is a human interpretation and probably wrong.

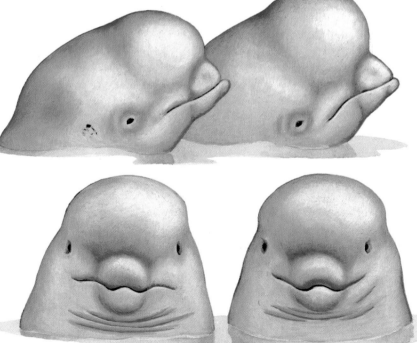

# LIFE CYCLE

The great sperm whale is a seasonal breeder, although matings and births are spread over a few months. In the Southern Hemisphere matings are in December and January. The females are pregnant for about fourteen months, so they give birth in February or March of the following year. In the Northern Hemisphere these dates differ by about four to six months.

After the calf is born, the mother feeds it on milk for two years or more, then rests for a year or two. The average young female produces a calf every four or five years. This is one of the slowest reproductive rates of any mammal.

At mating time, male sperm whales often battle with each other for the right to mate with the

All illustrations Philip Hood/Wildlife Art Agency

Godfrey Merlen/Oxford Scientific Films

## AGGRESSIVE MALES

At breeding time bull sperm whales often clash. They head-butt each other with tremendous dull thuds. Sometimes they try to slash and bite with their lower jaws. They may damage or lose their teeth, and even crack and break the long, slim jawbone.

Male narwhals also fight by jousting with each other using the extraordinary "tusk," often inflicting serious damage.

### MATING

*When sperm whales mate* (top left) *they do so belly to belly with the female on top and the bull supporting her from below.*

### PODS

*Female sperm whales live in groups with their calves and juveniles.*

females. After mating, the baby develops in the female's womb. It is born tail first, as in other whales, and at once follows its instincts to swim to the surface and breathe through its blowhole. The mother may initially support the new calf and nudge it to the surface, since it takes some practice to coordinate swimming, surfacing, and breathing.

The mother's mammary glands are contoured into her underside, for streamlining. The nipples protrude through long folds of skin, called mammary slits, only when the baby is feeding. The milk is squirted out by the mother, rather than being sucked in by the youngster. The newborn sperm whale is a big baby with an appetite to match, drinking 45 lb (20 kg) of milk daily.

The dwarf and pygmy sperm whales follow similar life cycles, although, being much smaller, the timings are relatively shorter. Gestation is about nine and eleven months respectively.

Belugas mate in late winter or early spring, and the calves are born fourteen months later, in the next summer. Belugas gather in shallow bays and estuaries to give birth. The mother leaves the main group for a week or two to produce and nurse her offspring. She may be accompanied by a younger female, probably a daughter from a previous mating. Young belugas swim so close to their mothers for the first year or two that the two almost seem to be joined together. The mother is very protective and charges at predators or intruders. The average time between calves is three years.

Narwhals follow a similar breeding pattern to belugas, but they do not seek shallow water, producing their calves in deeper inlets and fjords.

Breeding information for beaked whales is scarce. It seems that northern bottlenose whales have a pregnancy of around one year. New calves are 10–11.5 ft (3–3.5 m) long, arrive in early summer, and are weaned after about a year. Females produce a calf every two or three years, between the ages of about 10 and 25 years. ■

## FROM BIRTH TO DEATH

### SPERM WHALE

| | |
|---|---|
| **GESTATION:** 14–15 MONTHS | **SEXUAL MATURITY FOR FEMALE:** |
| **NUMBER OF YOUNG:** 1 | 7–12 YEARS OR 26–30 FT (8–9 M) IN |
| **LENGTH AT BIRTH:** 13 FT (4 M) | LENGTH |
| **WEIGHT AT BIRTH:** 1.1–2.2 TONS | **SEXUAL MATURITY FOR MALE:** |
| (1–2 TONNES) | 17–20 YEARS OR 40 FT (12 M) |
| **WEANING:** UP TO 2 YEARS | **LONGEVITY:** UP TO 60–70 YEARS |

### BELUGA WHALE

| | |
|---|---|
| **GESTATION:** 14–15 MONTHS | |
| **NUMBER OF YOUNG:** 1 | **INDEPENDENCE:** 3–5 YEARS |
| **LENGTH AT BIRTH:** 5 FT (1.5 M) | **SEXUAL MATURITY FOR FEMALE:** |
| **WEIGHT AT BIRTH:** 88–175 LB | 4–7 YEARS |
| (40–80 KG) | **SEXUAL MATURITY FOR MALE:** |
| **WEANING:** UP TO 2 YEARS | 7–9 YEARS |
| | **LONGEVITY:** 25–40 YEARS |

# SAVING THE WHALES

HUNTED FOR MORE THAN SIX CENTURIES, MANY SPECIES WERE BROUGHT TO THE EDGE OF EXTINCTION. CONSERVATION MEASURES HAVE NOW BEEN IN PLACE FOR 50 YEARS, BUT HOW SAFE IS THE WHALES' FUTURE?

People have been killing whales for survival for centuries. Native peoples of the coastal north hunted whales, seals, and similar sea creatures and used various parts of their bodies for food, fuels, clothing, and tools.

On a small scale, local whaling could cope and remain stable. But large-scale commercial whaling led to mass slaughter, which has decimated the populations of many species of baleen (whalebone) whales and some toothed whales, too. Commercial whaling began as far back as the 12th century and gained major momentum in the early 18th century, when Atlantic whaling fleets started to hunt sperm

**IN SOME CULTURES PEOPLE ARE STILL DEPENDENT ON THE WHALE FOR FOOD, FUEL, AND CLOTHING**

whales farther offshore. The first commercial hunting of sperm whales by Americans was recorded in 1712. Within a few decades, whaling ships were catching thousands of sperm whale each year.

Sperm whales had added advantages for whalers. They are among the whales that float when dead. They gather to support a sick or wounded companion, which made it possible to kill most of the pod after the first one had been harpooned. And the spermaceti oil in the head was valued as a high-quality lubricant.

The slaughter continued into the 19th century, with an American sperm-whaling fleet of more than 700 boats. In the 1860s the populations in the North Atlantic crashed. Luckily for the whales, reserves of oil were discovered under the ground in the United States at about this time, and petroleum and its products gradually began to replace the whale products, especially in oil for

lamps, but commercial whaling continued well into the 20th century.

## COMMERCIAL WHALING

It was a rough, tough life on board the old whaling ships. Voyages lasted up to four years, until the barrels in the holds were full of oil, blubber, spermaceti, and other whale products. The whale was harpooned by hand from a small row boat. As it swam and dived, it would tow the boat by the harpoon line at high speed through the foaming white waves, on the so-called Nantucket sleigh ride.

Male sperm whales, in particular, would ram boats, smash them with their enormous heads or thrashing flukes, and even crush the men in their powerful jaws.

*Employees at a large whaling station in the Azores (right) about to cut up a sperm whale.*

*Every part of a sperm whale was used. Even its teeth were carved by the whalers to pass the time.*

Ken Lucas/Planet Earth Pictures

Tony Martin/Oxford Scientific Films

*This map shows the main whaling areas of the world up to 1985.*

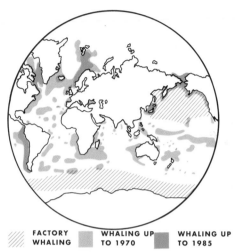

| FACTORY WHALING | WHALING UP TO 1970 | WHALING UP TO 1985 |

Thousands of whales had already lost their lives to the whalers by the time Svend Foyn from Norway had developed a harpoon with an explosive head, and a cannon gun to fire it, in the 1860s. Ships were also being equipped with engines and propellers, rather than sails. By the early 1900s, new uses had been found for whale oil, and massive factory ships with fleets of catcher boats were scouring all oceans for whales. The baleen species suffered most. Even so, the catch of sperm whales rose to 30,000 in the period 1963–64.

*Having injured one sperm whale, the whalers waited for the other pod members to form a protective circle around it, called the Marguerite formation. They, too, were then picked off.*

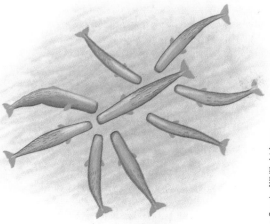

Barry Croucher/Wildlife Art Agency

2363

ENDANGERED SPECIES

The whale's carcass was tied next to the mother ship and the blubber "blanket" was stripped off with sharp blades on broomstick-sized handles, a process called flensing. It was cut into blocks and melted down in large heated iron pots called try-pots. The sperm whale's head was slit open, and buckets were dipped in to ladle out the spermaceti.

### WHALE CONSERVATION

The damage done by commercial whaling was obvious from a very early stage. Species by species, area by area, the whales disappeared. By the mid- and late 19th century, sperm whales had all but vanished in some areas of the North and South Atlantic. In the 1930s the same thing had happened to these whales in the Pacific. The whales

---

BELUGAS ARE DISAPPEARING IN SOME PARTS OF THEIR RANGE, SUCH AS IN THE GULF OF ST. LAWRENCE

---

could not replace themselves because of their very slow breeding rates.

The whalers then began to take smaller species, such as bottlenose whales and belugas, in faster boats and with more effective harpoons. They used spotter planes and helicopters, and the sound-echoes of sonar, to locate their quarry.

### INDUSTRIAL SUICIDE

In the 1930s more than 30,000 whales were killed each year, until World War II disturbed their business. As commerce and industry recovered from

---

## WHALE PRODUCTS

Almost every scrap of a whale's body can be used in some way. Listed here are some of them.
• Blubber produced oil for lamps; later for margarine, soaps, paints, and lubricants.
• Spermaceti was used for high-quality lubricating oils, in cosmetics, candles, and polishes.
• Ambergris, found in the guts of some sperm whales, is used as a base, stabilizer, and enhancer in fine perfumes.
• Whale meat is eaten in some areas.
• The skin of belugas and narwhals is made into thongs, boots, and laces.
• Whale cartilages were used to produce glues.
• Bones were ground up for fertilizer.
• Other parts were put into pet foods.

David Woodfall/NHPA

# CURRENT THREATS TO WHALES

For the time being, mass whaling has disappeared as the main threat to sperm whales, white whales, and beaked whales, and some populations are starting to build up again.

Most species of beaked whales have little to do with humans. They live in the middle of the oceans, as far as they can be from our activities. If they are threatened, it is by general problems facing all mid-oceanic life, such as chemical pollution and, very rarely, being trapped by fishnets. The same applies to sperm whales.

A few types of toothed whales face more immediate threats. Belugas, in particular, are affected by our activities because of their inshore habitats. The busy waters flowing into the Gulf of St. Lawrence illustrate several of the dangers. Resting belugas are often injured by ships. The boat traffic causes general disturbance and background stress. Chemical pollutants are washed in from farms and factories and get into the food chains. Belugas, being large predators, are at the top of the food chains. The chemicals become concentrated in their bodies by a process called biomagnification. Some belugas are thought to be sick or dying prematurely due to

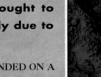

DEAD BABY SPERM WHALE STRANDED ON A BEACH IN NEW SOUTH WALES, AUSTRALIA.

## CONSERVATION MEASURES

People are now much more whale-aware. We know more than ever about the fascinating lives and social behavior of these mammalian cousins.

As the whales' situation changes, so do organizations concerned with them. The Whale Conservation Institute is located at 191 Weston Road, Lincoln, Massachusetts, 01773. A recognized global leader in whale research since 1967, WCI is dedicated to the protection of whales through groundbreaking research and international education initiatives.

the cocktail of toxic chemicals. A few have been literally radioactive. From previously large groups in the Gulf, only about 500 remain.

Pygmy and dwarf sperm whales are sometimes caught and drowned in gill nets set by commercial fishermen in the Indian and Pacific Oceans. They may benefit from the controls and changes in this type of fishing, brought about by concern for dolphins killed in the same way.

Dams and wells are another threat. Built across rivers for hydroelectric power, they alter the flow and temperature of the water in sensitive places where belugas give birth to their calves. Oil wells, pipelines, and terminals in coastal areas pose the possible danger of oil spills. Belugas are still hunted by local people under controlled whaling agreements. During the 1980s, around 1,000–2,000 were caught each year.

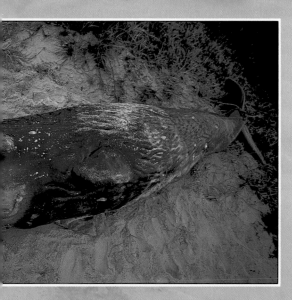

Inset Frord Kristo/Planet Earth Pictures

Recent studies of a wide diversity of species provide compelling evidence that global chemical accumulation threatens humanity and the natural world, but there is no measurement of the degree of this threat. The Whale Conservation Institute's newest initiative, the Global Ecotox Program, will provide the first ever baseline study of how chemical contaminants vary globally.

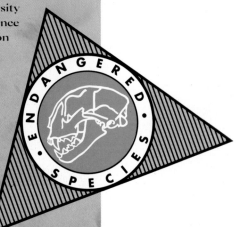

## TOOTHED WHALES IN DANGER

CITES, THE CONVENTION ON INTERNATIONAL TRADE IN ENDANGERED SPECIES, OPENED FOR SIGNING IN 1974. ALL CETACEANS—WHALES, DOLPHINS, AND PORPOISES—ARE ON THE CITES LISTS. TRADE IN THEM OR THEIR PRODUCTS IS LEGAL ONLY WITH SPECIAL LICENSES AND PERMISSION.

| ALL WHALES | CATEGORY K |
|---|---|

THE IUCN PRODUCES OFFICIAL LISTS OF THREATENED ANIMALS. ALL OF THE TOOTHED WHALES COVERED HERE, INCLUDING THE THREE SPECIES OF SPERM WHALES, TWO SPECIES OF WHITE WHALES, AND EIGHTEEN TO NINETEEN SPECIES OF BEAKED WHALES, ARE LISTED IN CATEGORY K. THIS MEANS THAT THEY ARE SUSPECTED TO BE IN ONE OF THE THREATENED CATEGORIES— RARE, VULNERABLE, OR ENDANGERED—BUT THERE IS INSUFFICIENT DATA FOR A MORE PRECISE PLACING.

Zig Leszczynski/Oxford Scientific Films

the war, some farsighted people realized that the slaughter could not go on. Unless there were guidelines and controls, whale populations would become too small to exploit successfully. Whaling as an industry would kill itself. On the issues of conservation, some whale species might even become extinct. Whalers must control their activities for their own long-term advantage.

The International Whaling Commission (IWC) was set up in 1946 (see page 2367) to cope with the problems. It gradually introduced lists of protected species, closed areas of sea where whaling should not take place, and opened and closed seasons.

### SAVE THE WHALES
In the 1950s and 1960s, scientists discovered more about whales and their behavior and social life. Through TV programs and articles in the press, the public began to understand what happened when a whale was harpooned. After all, it is a mammal—a warm-blooded creature like ourselves. It felt pain and cried out in agony. Baby whales saw their mothers killed and cut up.

People began to identify with whales and speak out against the killing. The focus was on the great baleen whales, but even the fearsome-looking sperm whales came in for sympathy. Surely there were more humane alternatives to whale products? Save the Whale campaigns became popular as organizations such as the World Wide Fund for Nature (WWF), Greenpeace, and Friends of the Earth took up interest. People also began to value live whales, taking trips and vacations to watch and even touch them (see Whale Watch, page 2367).

At the same time, the numbers of whales were falling so low that whaling was no longer profitable.

Ben Osborne/Oxford Scientific Films

The United States and many European nations decided to call a halt for business reasons as well as a result of public pressure. During the 1920s and 1930s, the main whaling countries were Great Britain, Norway, Holland, and the United States. By the 1960s they were the former U.S.S.R., Japan, Iceland, and Norway.

### THE OTHER SIDE OF THE COIN

But it was not a simple matter of good and bad. For some nations, such as Japan and Norway, whaling was not only big business but also a traditional way of life. It brought employment. Men and women had jobs in catching and processing whales, earning money to support their families. Income from the export of whale products contributed to national wealth. As whaling declined, whole communities were disrupted and

*A whale cemetery at Port Lockroy, Antarctica* (above). *This was once a base for whalers.*

*A beluga whale performing with its trainer at a Vancouver aquarium.*

traditional ways of life disappeared.

In the 1970s, the IWC gradually gained more member nations and more influence in the global community. The World Conservation Union, founded in 1948, drew attention to the dangers that some whale species had become so rare that they would die out altogether.

The United States had banned the import of whale products in 1970. In 1972, its Marine Mammal Protection Act prohibited commercial exploitation of whales in U.S. waters, except for subsistence and traditional uses by native people such as the Inuit, Aleuts, Amerindians, and Alaskans.

A FACTORY SHIP COULD SEPARATE, PROCESS, AND STORE THE DIFFERENT PRODUCTS OF ONE WHALE IN LESS THAN AN HOUR

Also in 1972, the United Nations held a conference on the Human Environment in Stockholm, Sweden. Among many other proposals, it suggested a ten-year moratorium on whaling, although this was not taken up at the time by the IWC.

Many other nations were taking the same twin steps: increasing limits on catching whales, and increasing limits for the trade of whale products. This has been achieved partly through the CITES International Trade Agreement (see page 2365). Some countries joined the IWC simply to speak out against whaling.

In 1982 the IWC voted to phase out all commercial whaling by the end of the 1985 season. The moratorium is still in place, and there are increasing moves to extend it to smaller cetaceans such as dolphins and porpoises. ■

## ALONGSIDE MAN

It seems that everywhere the whales go, humans go, too. From being hunted almost to extinction, the whales have become a major tourist attraction all over the world. Special nature tours with boat trips to whale areas are becoming more and more popular.

For other vacationers, it is to the aquarium that they flock to see whales and dolphins performing. Although increasingly controversial, whale exhibits present these marine mammals as ambassadors for their species, and the shows have contributed significantly to public opinion against whaling.

Heather Angel

# INTO THE FUTURE

The problem with whales is that they are difficult to count. They roam over large areas and stay submerged for long periods. As a result, estimates of population sizes vary enormously, even when made by reputable scientific surveys.

The great sperm whale was always, and still is, one of the most common large whales. Despite hundreds of thousands being killed, its numbers are not critical. Estimates vary from half a million to approaching two million worldwide. However, with its slow breeding rate, this will probably be

## PREDICTION

### WHALE WORTH

*Supporters of whale-watching say that it is educational, scientific, recreational, and pleasurable. The hope is that all nations will see that whales are worth more when alive than dead.*

the species that takes longest to recover from the ravages of commercial whaling.

Both pygmy and dwarf sperm whales are uncommon, but they have probably always been so. Belugas may number around 50,000–60,000. There are probably similar numbers of narwhals. Bottlenose whales seem to have survived reasonably well and probably exist in large numbers. ∎

## GLOBAL MONITORING

The International Whaling Commission (IWC) was set up in 1946 to monitor and regulate whaling on a global basis. There were fourteen member nations. However, the commission had limited legal powers, and none at all over nonmember nations, so large-scale whaling continued in many areas. By the early 1980s public opinion was turning against whaling. In 1982 the member nations of the IWC, then numbering thirty-eight, voted to ban all commercial whaling after 1985.

The IWC regularly reviews its ban, with much heated debate. The IWC Scientific Committee compiles reports on whale populations, and both pro- and anti-whalers produce other scientific evidence to support their case. In 1993, at its meeting in Kyoto, Japan, the IWC voted to extend the moratorium, which is still in effect. Norway has resumed small-scale commercial whaling, and it has been sanctioned by other nations.

## WHALE WATCH

*Have you ever stroked a whale? Whale-watching, and even whale-touching for the more docile species, is now a leisure industry. It began commercially in 1955 along the southern coast of California. By 1994, some 35 countries and five million people were taking part. Tours vary from a short trip along the coast to a two-week cruise around Antarctica, in crafts from rubber inflatables, dinghies, fishing boats, and cruise ships to aircraft. Oceanic toothed whales are among the rarer sightings, and belugas and narwhals are very popular.*

*Whale-watching is now well established in North America, although new areas are being established, such as Alaska, Washington State, Florida, and the Caribbean. In South America, the potential is enormous. In Europe, tours around northern Norway and the Canary Islands have been spectacularly successful. Paradoxically, the Japanese whale-watching industry has also grown rapidly.*

Illustration Steve Kingston

# WOLVERINES

Both the wolverine and the skunk are members of the mammal order Carnivora and the family Mustelidae. This family is broken down into five subfamilies; the skunks make up one of these, and the wolverine belongs to the subfamily that includes the martens and true weasels.

**ORDER**

*Carnivora*
(carnivores)

**FAMILY**
*Mustelidae*
(weasels)

**SUBFAMILIES**
*Mustelinae*
(weasels and allies)
*Mephitinae*
(skunks)

**WOLVERINE GENUS**
*one*

**SKUNK GENERA**
*three*

**SPECIES**
*one wolverine
thirteen skunks*

ZEFA

# BRUTE FORCE AND INSOLENCE

### THE FABLED FEROCITY OF THE WOLVERINE AND THE NOTORIOUS STINK BOMBS OF THE SKUNKS ENABLE THESE UNLIKELY RELATIVES TO GO WHERE THEY PLEASE, CONFIDENT OF THEIR NEAR-IMMUNITY TO ATTACK

In the eerie twilight of a northern forest, a stocky animal emerges from the trees and lopes across the soft snow of a clearing: a wolverine. Halfway across, it stops, sniffs, and slips into the shadows beneath a spruce tree. It begins to dig, raking the snow back with broad feet to reveal the half-eaten remains of a roe deer, killed over a week before by a lynx. The meat is frozen solid, but to the wolverine this is a small detail; its jaws can deal with far tougher fare.

The animal sets to work, and before long the carcass has been reduced to a dark stain in the snow. Food is scarce in the northern winter, and it may be many days before the wolverine feeds again.

#### SUPERMARTEN
With its heavy limbs, short ears, and dense, dark fur, the wolverine looks like a bear but is actually a giant mustelid—a relative of the weasels and stoats. Most mustelids are slender, sinuous creatures

adapted for pursuing their prey through burrows and tight crevices—a body form exemplified by the weasel, with its almost snakelike proportions. The wolverine, however, has become a brawny, open-country predator and scavenger, trading suppleness for stamina and sleek stealth for sheer brute force.

This emphasis on muscle is shared by another group of mustelids, the badgers, which some zoologists believe to be close relatives. But badgers are specialists at digging, with short, sturdy limbs and raking claws; the wolverine can certainly dig, but it shows more aptitude for climbing trees, scampering

---

AT UP TO 55 LB (25 KG), THE WOLVERINE IS ONE OF THE HEAVIEST MUSTELIDS, ABLE TO BRING DOWN A FULL-GROWN REINDEER

---

up the rough bark with the agility of a cat. It also favors warm-blooded prey, whereas true badgers prefer to feed on roots, insects, and earthworms. For these and other reasons, the wolverine is normally regarded as a giant relative of the tree-dwelling, predatory martens: a supermarten.

### SIZE IS EVERYTHING

The size of the wolverine may have been influenced by its harsh environment: the chilly forests and arctic tundra of northern Scandinavia, Siberia, and Canada. Animals that live in cold

Hans Reinhard/Bruce Coleman Ltd.

Erwin & Peggy Bauer/Bruce Coleman Ltd.

*The skunk's bold coat delivers an unmistakable warning to all who approach it* (above).

*Largest of the skunks, the striped species* (left) *is also the most common, with a wide range to match.*

Ken Cole/Natural Science Photos

*The wolverine* (above), *also known as the skunk bear, has much in common with its smelly cousins.*

habitats tend to be bigger than their more pampered relatives—Arctic wolves, for example, are larger than the wolves found in the Mediterranean area. Bulk has two advantages in subzero conditions: It conserves an animal's core body temperature and it increases its capacity to take large meals at long intervals. The subpolar winter is long and hard, and many prey animals migrate or go underground to escape it. A predator like the wolverine may go for days without a decent meal, then strike it lucky by finding the carcass of a reindeer. It must be able to make the most of its opportunity by gorging itself and leaving as little as possible to be discovered by other scavengers; the bigger it is, the more it can eat.

It is also equipped with the tools for the job. Even allowing for its size, its premolars—the cheek teeth—are the largest found among the mustelids, set in immensely strong jaws closed by powerful muscles. These cheek teeth have evolved into meat-shearing carnassials, but their sheer size gives them the strength to crush bone as well as slice through skin, flesh, and sinew. In this respect the wolverine is the northern equivalent of the hyenas, and it exploits its advantages in the same way: by scavenging remains that other predators reject as inedible. Such an ability to make a meal out of scraps is a valuable aid to survival through the barren months of winter.

This capacity to eat the uneatable has given the wolverine a reputation for having a huge appetite. Seeing wolverines finishing off the remains of large animals, such as sheep and reindeer, people assumed that they devoured such carcasses at a sitting—a clearly impossible feat, given the size of the animal's stomach. Yet the wolverine was widely believed to be capable of eating almost anything, in immense quantities, earning it the name by which it is still known in some areas: the glutton.

The wolverine has also been credited with extreme savagery, with rather more reason: If it comes across a larger predator, such as a bear, feeding at a kill, it is quite capable of driving it off ferociously; it defends its own interests with equal vigor. In general, however, it reserves such energetic displays for practical purposes and rarely launches into an unprovoked attack. Despite this, it is widely regarded as a dangerous animal and, like all large carnivores, has been hunted relentlessly on the flimsiest of pretexts.

### SKUNKS

Thickset and mean-tempered, the wolverine has few enemies except humans. Smaller mustelids, however, are no match for big predators, and one group in particular—the skunks—has developed one of the most effective defense systems of all.

A skunk's weaponry is universally notorious: a foul cocktail of chemicals sprayed with perfect precision from its anal glands (see Defenses, page 2384). But the skunk's unmistakable looks usually discourage attackers: All skunks sport a conspicuous pattern of black and white spots or stripes, and they rarely bother to conceal themselves while active. At the sight of that harlequin coat, most predators—including humans—beat a hasty retreat.

The 13 species of skunks are all found in the Americas, in a diverse range of habitats from southern Canada to Patagonia. There are three main types: the striped skunks, spotted skunks, and hognosed skunks. These are classified respectively in three genera: *Mephitis* (meh-FEET-iss), *Spilogale* (SPEEL-o-gahl), and *Conepatus* (con-eh-PAT-us).

The skunks originated in Eurasia, and fossil remains of one of their ancestors, *Miomephitis* (mie-o-meh-FEET-iss), have been found in rocks laid down some 22 million years ago. Between five and ten million years ago they reached America via the dry land that once bridged Siberia and Alaska. The lineage died out in Eurasia but thrived in America, due perhaps to the absence of small badgers. For skunks live very much like badgers, foraging for small prey among the undergrowth and scratching up insect grubs and worms with their foreclaws, and the presence of species such as the ferret badgers of eastern Asia might have presented competition. In ecological terms, skunks occupy the small badger niche in the New World, while small badgers occupy the skunk niche in the Old World. ■

# WOLVERINE
*Gulo gulo (GOO-lo GOO-lo)*

**The biggest of all terrestrial mustelids, the wolverine looks like a small bear with a bushy tail. Found in the forests and tundra regions of the far north, it is sparsely distributed over huge areas of wilderness. It is one of the most poorly understood of all the larger carnivores.**

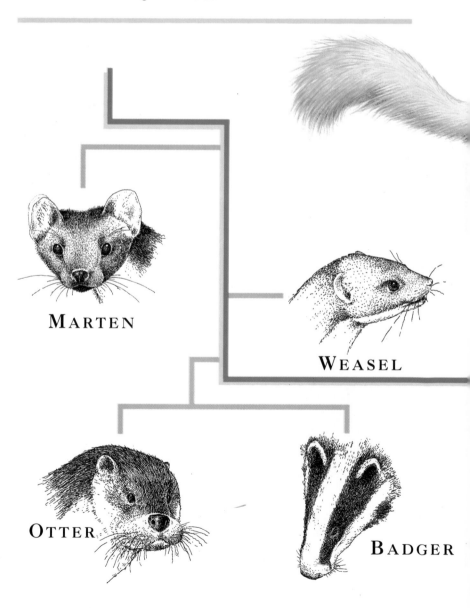

MARTEN

WEASEL

OTTER

BADGER

# THE WOLVERINE'S FAMILY TREE

The weasel family includes the otters, badgers, weasels and their relatives, and skunks. The wolverine is a single species allied to the weasels, in the subfamily Mustelinae (must-ELL-in-ie), and appears to be most closely related to the tree-dwelling martens. The skunks are classified in a subfamily of their own—the Mephitinae (mef-IT-in-ie)—and are grouped into three genera: the spotted skunks, the hog-nosed skunks, and the striped and hooded skunks.

## SPOTTED SKUNKS
### Spilogale
### (SPEEL-o-gahl)

**The four small species of spotted skunks are black with slim white stripes or spots. They have a habit of "handstanding" to warn off enemies before spraying. They range from the southeastern and western United States to Costa Rica.**

## HOG-NOSED SKUNK
### Conepatus
### (con-eh-PAT-us)

**The seven species of hog-nosed skunks are found from the southern United States to the southern tip of South America. They are distinguished by their bare, elongated snouts, which they use for rooting in the ground for insects and other small animals.**

## STRIPED SKUNK
## HOODED SKUNK
### Mephitis
### (meh-FEET-iss)

**The striped skunk is the largest and most adaptable of the subfamily, found in habitats ranging from the chilly Canadian forests to the deserts of Mexico. The similar hooded skunk has an all-white back and is an elusive native of the southwestern United States.**

MUSTELIDS

BEAR

DINGO

CARNIVORES

Color illustrations Simon Turvey/Wildlife Art Agency

2373

# ANATOMY:
# WOLVERINE
### THE

The wolverine has a head-and-body length of up to 33 in (83 cm) with a 8 in (20 cm) tail. Females average 22 lb (10 kg); males average 33 lb (15 kg), but can weigh up to 55 lb (25 kg).

## THE MUZZLE

is short and powerful, with a sensitive nose and strong jaws. The widely set eyes are small, as are the ears, and the animal relies mainly on scent to find food.

## THE THICK FUR

is coarse and long, with a dense, woolly underfur to keep out the cold. A band of light brown extends down each flank from the shoulder to the base of the tail. The facial mask is dark, with a pale forehead.

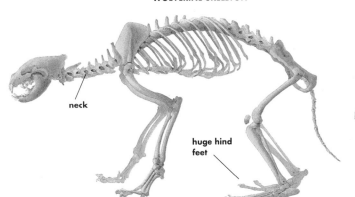

hind foot

fore-foot

**WOLVERINE**

hind foot          forefoot

**STRIPED SKUNK**

## THE FEET

are broad and partly webbed, with long claws. The soles are thickly haired to improve their grip on ice. The wolverine walks on the soles of its feet, and their width stops the animal from sinking into soft snow.

## THE LEGS

are powerful, enabling the wolverine to keep moving all day without tiring—essential for an animal with such a huge home range.

---

**X**

R
A
Y

The wolverine's skeleton reflects its heavy, muscular build. The neck is stout, and the general proportions are more bearlike than mustelid. The bones in the hind feet are greatly elongated.

**WOLVERINE SKELETON**

neck

huge hind feet

**SKUNK SKELETON**

Much smaller than the wolverine, the skunks nevertheless share its basic conformation.

long tail

tapering rib cage

**SPOTTED SKUNK**
Black with white stripes on the back and sides, plus smaller stripes and spots on the rump.

**HOG-NOSED SKUNK**
Black except for a white "cape" from brow to tail. Alternatively, black with two white stripes.

**STRIPED SKUNK**
Black with a varying degree of white areas, among which there are no stray black hairs.

## FACT FILE:
### THE WOLVERINE

### CLASSIFICATION

GENUS: *GULO*
SPECIES: *GULO*

### SIZE

HEAD–BODY LENGTH: UP TO 33 IN (83 CM)
TAIL LENGTH: 8 IN (20 CM)
AVERAGE WEIGHT/MALE: 33 LB (15 KG)
AVERAGE WEIGHT/FEMALE: 22 LB (10 KG)
WEIGHT AT BIRTH: 3.5 OZ (100 G)
FEMALES ARE ABOUT 10 PERCENT SHORTER THAN MALES AND 30 PERCENT LIGHTER IN WEIGHT

### COLORATION

DUSKY BROWN WITH DARK MASK AND PALE BROWN BROW; DISTINCT PALE BAND EXTENDING FROM SHOULDER TO RUMP ON EACH FLANK, JOINING OVER BASE OF TAIL
CUBS: WHITE TO SANDY YELLOW

### FEATURES

POWERFUL, BEARLIKE BUILD
BUSHY TAIL
BROAD, STRONGLY CLAWED FEET
AWKWARD GAIT

**THE BUSHY TAIL**

distinguishes the wolverine from the bears, which it otherwise resembles. The tail is usually carried low.

The powerful jaw muscles of the wolverine are anchored to the prominent crest on its skull, providing the leverage to crack the limb bones of reindeer and reach the rich marrow within. The big, bladelike premolar teeth, called the carnassials, are principally adapted for shearing flesh and sinew, but they are also strong enough to crush even the thickest of bones.

**WOLVERINE SKULL**

eye socket

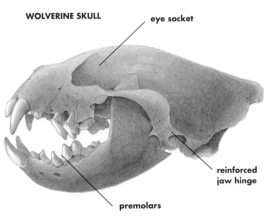

reinforced jaw hinge

premolars

**SKUNK SKULL**

canines

The skunk's skull is typical of mustelids, with a heavy, strongly hinged jaw, blunt nasal area, and long, sharp canines.

# FOUL AND FEARLESS

## BOTH THE WOLVERINE AND SKUNKS ARE OPPORTUNISTS, READY TO TAKE ANY FOOD ON OFFER. FEW PREDATORS WILL DARE TRY TO ROB THEM OF THEIR PRIZE

Walking toward evening, the skunk hunts by night, when its prey is also active. It ambles through the brushwood, pausing to investigate fallen logs or turn over leaf litter. It rarely roams far, particularly in summer when reptiles, insects, and fruit are abundant. By day it retires to its den, usually in a burrow but often in the nearest dry hollow.

Winter brings with it a scarcity of prey, and striped skunks may huddle together in a single underground den for weeks on end. They spend most of their time asleep, but will wake up to forage during mild spells; in general, however, they get through the cold months by living off body fat built up by heavy feeding during the autumn. They emerge much thinner in the spring.

Farther north, in wolverine country, conditions are harsh in the extreme. But this arctic marauder stays active all year, and even in winter it may travel up to 28 miles (45 km) a day through the snowy forests, often covering 6 miles (10 km) or more without stopping to rest. Like the skunks, it is most active by night, denning by day in a hollow beneath a fallen tree, in a burrow dug by some other animal, or in a cave made comfortable with a rough bed of leaves or grass. The arctic winter is shrouded by endless night, and the summer is a season of permanent daylight, so the wolverine settles into a cycle of three to four hours of activity followed by a similar period of sleep, moving from den to den as it treks through its vast home range. ■

*A striped skunk sits up on its haunches to sample the breeze for a scent of prey (below).*

## ![in]SIGHT

### COLD COMFORT

**Active in winter, the wolverine must keep its vital organs at about 98.6°F (37°C), so it allows its limbs to cool down to well below the temperature of the body core. This conserves the heat where it is needed, while special adaptations enable the limbs to function even when cold.**

**The striped skunk, however, sleeps through the winter, allowing its whole body to cool to some 50°F (10°C) below normal. Its vital organs can tolerate this condition, which would almost certainly kill a wolverine.**

Pat Morris/Ardea

*Lumbering over the snow on its broad paws, a wolverine uncovers a food cache (right).*

Erwin & Peggy Bauer/Bruce Coleman Ltd.

# HABITATS

**The wolverine occurs in the northern taiga forests, extending into the Arctic tundra in summer. It also occurs farther south in Canada and the United States. The skunks are restricted to the New World. The striped skunk occurs from Canada to Mexico, the spotted skunks from the southern United States to Costa Rica, and the hog-nosed skunks from the southern United States to Patagonia.**

**B**etween them, the wolverine and skunks live in habitats as varied as Arctic tundra and baking deserts. The most successful species is the striped skunk, which ranges from the southern fringes of the Canadian forests to the deserts of northern Mexico. In between, it occurs in mountains, grassland, farmland, and even suburban areas. Above all it favors open woodland or forest edges, where food is in rich supply.

In the south of its range the striped skunk often comes across the hooded, spotted, and hog-nosed skunks. In general the various species exploit their domains in different ways and can share them without compromising each other's chances of survival.

The other species are more restricted in range than the striped skunk. Several spotted skunks—the western, southern, and pygmy species—occur in the western United States and Mexico, while the eastern spotted skunk inhabits the southeast and central United States. Spotted skunks favor rocky, scrubby, and wooded habitats, avoiding wetlands and dense forests. In these southern climes they stay active all year, but they tend to seek cover and rarely emerge by day. Although they generally lodge in burrows and crevices, they can climb well and may den in tree hollows up to 33 ft (10 m) above the ground.

The hog-nosed skunks are found chiefly in Central and South America, although two of the seven species occur in the southern United States. Like the spotted skunks, they shun dense forest, and even the Amazonian skunk prefers grassland and open woods. Some live in craggy and mountainous areas, and the Andes skunk occurs at elevations of at least 13,000 ft

*Spotted skunks do not mind sharing a daytime den from time to time. Here, a few nestle in a crevice* (above).

*A wolverine slips out of a temporary den for a night of foraging* (below). *Unlike the skunks, this mustelid dens in solitude.*

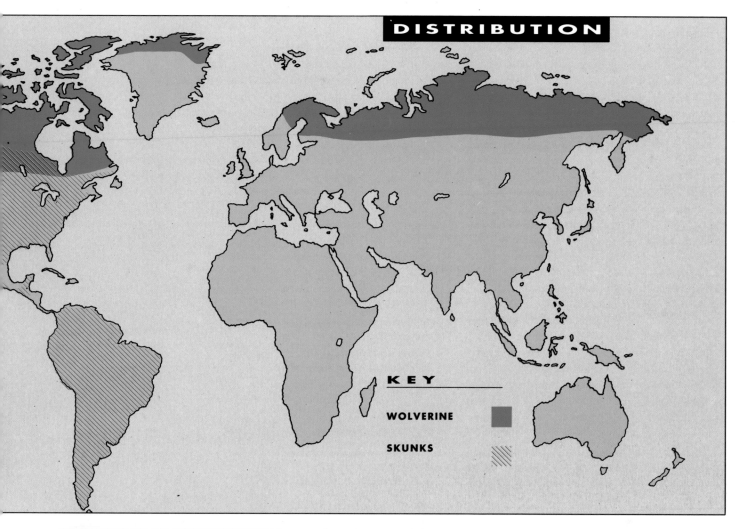

# DISTRIBUTION

**KEY**

WOLVERINE

SKUNKS

# KEY FACTS

- If a skunk decides to use another animal's burrow as a den, it is quite capable of evicting the original occupant, or even killing it. Occasionally, however, the owner stays in residence and the two animals share the premises, each occupying its own section.

- The northern habitats of the wolverine experience very low rainfall or snowfall, and in any other climate they would be deserts. But since the land derives so little heat from the sun there is very little evaporation, and most of the rain or snow that does fall simply accumulates as lakes, swamps, glaciers, and snowdrifts.

- The striped skunk's strategy of lying dormant in hard winters does not enable it to live in the far north where the wolverine roams, since the animal could not store up sufficient fat reserves in the short northern summer season to last it through the long winter. On the tundra, even small resident mammals, such as lemmings, have to stay active all year-round to survive.

(4,000 m). They often den in rock crevices or use tree hollows and burrows dug by other animals. They stay active all year, for although the winter is cold in the mountains and the far south, it rarely drives the animals into a state of torpor.

## TUNDRA AND TAIGA

The wolverine occurs across the northern forests and Arctic fringes of Scandinavia, Siberia, Canada, and Alaska, as well as the rugged Pacific states of the United States. On a standard world map its range seems vast and sprawling, but a map centered on the North Pole shows it as a well-defined ring around the frozen heart of the High Arctic.

This ring consists of two basic types of habitats. Nearest the center, at the edge of the Arctic Ocean, the Greenland ice sheets, and the northern islands, lies the tundra. Here, the subsoil is forever frozen; this permafrost layer impedes drainage, destabilizing the topsoil and creating myriad pools, streams, and swamps, where large trees cannot grow. In the brief but intense Arctic summer, the surface layer thaws, allowing small, cold-resistant plants, such as grasses, mosses, and lichens, to set seed.

Farther from the Pole, the permafrost gives way to a marginal zone where hardy trees can take root in the looser soil, and the edge of the tundra is usually marked by a scattering of birches. Farther out still, the birch wood thickens and eventually gives way to a thick, evergreen forest of conifers such as pine and spruce, known in Siberia as the taiga.

The wolverine makes its home among the trees and mountains of the taiga, where there are maybe two frost-free months in the year. The winter can cool to -76°F (-60°C) in the heart of Siberia, but the trees provide windbreaks, and many animals bed down in the deep snow. The old or weak often succumb, however, and the wolverine sniffs out their remains. It also hunts the species that migrate south into the shelter of the forests in winter, often following them back into the tundra in summer.

Summer on the tundra can be a dazzling sight. The plants bloom, and the air hums with newly emerged insects. The insects attract migrant birds, which fly north to breed on the marshes. Reindeer move north from the forests to crop the grasses and mosses, and lemmings emerge from their winter retreats. In their turn the nesting birds, lemmings, and reindeer attract the predators: snowy owls, gyrfalcons, Arctic foxes, wolves—and wolverines.

## FOCUS ON

# THE TAIGA

**Much of the Northern Hemisphere, on the fringes of the Arctic, is cloaked in a vast, dark coniferous forest. This is often termed the boreal (northern) zone, but in Russia, where the forest covers over a third of the land area of the former Soviet Union, it is called the taiga. This is the home of the wolverine.**

**The taiga vegetation is dominated by evergreen firs, spruces and pines, deciduous larches, and, in more open places, birches. The evergreens cast a dense shade on the forest floor, as well as a thick carpet of needle litter. This gives rise to a cold, acid soil that support a few acid-tolerant plants such as bilberry, dwarf birch, mosses and lichens, and fungi. In poorly drained areas the ground is covered with a springy carpet of *Sphagnum* moss, which holds the water like a sponge. In places the sphagnum has built up to form great waterlogged peat bogs. The bog pools act as breeding grounds for mosquitoes, which hatch and take to the air in vast, bloodsucking swarms in summer.**

**The wolverine tends to favor rocky, well-drained terrain, where the insects are less numerous and dry denning sites are more easily found. The availability of food is more of a problem, particularly in winter, since, although these forests support flourishing populations of prey animals, many of these go underground beneath the thick snow in winter.**

## TEMPERATURE AND RAINFALL

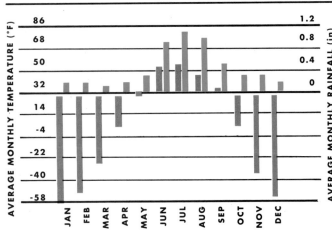

**TEMPERATURE**

**RAINFALL**

*In the eastern Siberian taiga, temperatures can fluctuate from -90°F (-68°C) in winter to almost 100°F (38°C) in summer. In the far north the rainfall is light, but the long, cold winters mean that the ground is marshy all year round.*

For a wolverine, summer on the tundra offers rich pickings among the colonies of ground-nesting birds and small mammals. The fact that most of these prey animals are breeding is a welcome bonus: The eggs and nestlings of the birds are easy meat, and the calves of reindeer and even musk ox are sometimes vulnerable. This summer picnic does not last long, however, and by September the migrants have started retreating south from the gathering darkness and plummeting temperatures. The tundra wolverines retreat with them, back into the forest and a different life. ∎

## NEIGHBORS

**Icy, marshy, and forbidding, the taiga would seem to be an unlikely habitat for wildlife, but the remote forests are in fact home to some of the world's most resilient opportunists.**

**CAPERCAILLIE**

*This large grouse is one of the most dramatic forest birds, famous for its courtship ritual in spring.*

**BEAVER**

*The beaver protects itself from the wolverine by surrounding its lodge with a deep, dammed lake.*

Philippe Henry/Oxford Scientific Films

# ENEMIES

### WOLF

A single wolf would not trouble a wolverine, but a pack could easily kill one if it tried to stand its ground.

### BROWN BEAR

Although a wolverine may try to drive a bear off its prey, it is often no match for this massive adversary.

### THE TAIGA

In Russia the taiga extends for over 6,000 miles (10,000 km) from the Baltic to the Pacific, and continues on the other side of the Bering Strait from Alaska to the Hudson Bay. It is the biggest forest in the world, composed mainly of cold-tolerant conifers such as spruce, fir, and pine. Many parts of it are still unexplored.

| GREAT GRAY OWL | MOOSE | GOSHAWK | LYNX | CROSSBILL |
|---|---|---|---|---|

Despite its great size, this superb bird of the northern forests feeds mainly on voles.

The largest of the deer, even this mighty creature occasionally falls victim to the wolverine.

The goshawk weaves skillfully through the forest in pursuit of grouse, hares, and other prey.

This small wildcat competes with the wolverine for food. Its populations are healthiest where humans are scarce.

The twisted bill of this finch enables it to pry open the cones of the taiga trees and lever out the tasty seeds.

# FOOD AND FEEDING

The wolverine is no high-profile predator; it cannot match the sinuous attack of a stoat, the stealth of a cat, or the tactical cunning of a wolf. Yet it does have one valuable asset as a hunter in the snowbound northern forests: It has big feet.

The wolverine is heavy, yet its broad feet with their thickly haired soles spread its weight so well on powdery snow that it barely sinks in at all. So while other animals flounder through the drifts, the wolverine can keep up a brisk canter over considerable distances. More importantly, it can outpace its prey. In summer, the wolverine can barely catch an Arctic hare. It generally picks on helpless, slow-moving prey, such as ground-nesting birds, lemmings, and voles. But on snow, a wolverine can pursue and kill an adult reindeer ten times its own weight, and it has been known to bring down a full-grown moose. It will even kill other predators such as foxes, martens, and the occasional lynx.

Old or sickly winter-weakened reindeer are no match for a wolverine, especially the Scandinavian domesticated reindeer that seem to be more vulnerable than their wild counterparts. In Canada, the wolverine feeds mainly on carrion in winter,

> ON ONE OCCASION, A WOLVERINE CHASED A LYNX UP A TREE, CLIMBED UP IN PURSUIT, PULLED IT DOWN, AND KILLED IT

although reindeer—dead and alive—still form the bulk of its winter diet.

The wolverine's favored tactic is the ambush. It will lurk behind a rock, or climb a tree and lie on a branch overhanging a reindeer trail, then leap onto its victim's back and cling on for 300 ft (100 m) or more with its stout claws. Eventually the quarry will lose its balance and be dragged down, to be torn apart by the wolverine's powerful jaws.

In winter the wolverine also preys on roe deer, wild sheep, hares, squirrels, voles, and ground birds such as capercaillies, willow grouse, and ptarmigan. Small game is killed with a neck bite and is usually bolted down at once. In the case of larger prey, the wolverine eats what it can, then buries the surplus under the snow or in marshy ground, or even hauls it up a tree. Wolverines can drag prey up to three times their own weight over rough terrain to hide it from other scavengers. A wolverine may return to the carcass within a few hours or ignore it for up to six months: Such caches are often made in autumn as a precaution against food shortages in the depths of winter.

*Erwin & Peggy Bauer/Bruce Coleman Ltd.*

*Having found a meal, the wolverine very rarely yields to other predators (above).*

*Main illustrations Robin Boutell/Wildlife Art Agency*

# PREY

*Almost any animal, alive or dead, offers the prospect of a meal for the wolverine. As well as small mammals and birds, it will tackle a young, old, or sickly reindeer or musk ox, given the opportunity.*

Prey illustrations Ruth Grewcock

**ARCTIC HARE**

**REINDEER**

In summer, food is more freely available. Some wolverines live almost exclusively on berries and nuts when they are available, but in general they take small mammals such as voles and lemmings, as well as insect grubs and carrion. On the arctic tundra they take the eggs and fledglings of ground-nesting birds, and they will also tackle unattended reindeer calves if they can. A hungry wolverine will drive fish into shallow water and scoop them out with its sharp claws, just like a grizzly bear.

Skunks are largely carnivorous. They often forage for scraps in urban areas, but they are not great scavengers. They cannot crush thick bones, and being small animals with modest appetites and occupying habitats where food is generally abundant, they can usually find enough to eat without resorting to the leavings of others. Small size has its compensations, particularly when you can scare away your enemies so easily. ■

**A REINDEER CALF**

*succumbs to a hungry*

*wolverine* (left).

## SNAKE KILLERS

Intriguingly, skunks show a marked taste for unfriendly prey. They often raid the nests of wasps and bees to steal larvae and honey, seemingly unconcerned by the stings. Some species attack and eat venomous snakes. Hog-nosed skunks in particular have a high immunity to snake venom: In one case a hog-nosed skunk was bitten ten times by a bushmaster—a normally lethal South American pit viper—and appeared to be unharmed. Spotted skunks seem to have a similar immunity to rattlesnake venom.

*The wolverine's jaws*

*can crush even the*

*thickest bone* (right).

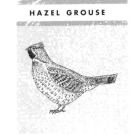

**ARCTIC LEMMING**

**HAZEL GROUSE**

**MUSK OX CALF**

**ARCTIC FOX**

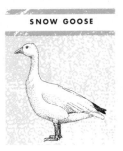

**SNOW GOOSE**

# DEFENSES

All the animals in the weasel family—including the wolverine—use scent spraying as a means of defense, but the skunks have refined the device into one of the most devastating defensive weapons in the animal kingdom. It is so effective that skunks are virtually immune to attack from most mature, experienced predators, and young animals that have never encountered a skunk before soon learn to associate those stripes and spots with a very unpleasant experience indeed.

Skunks are armed with their repellent odor from the age of one month or even less. The scent

---

THE SKUNK'S GLAND MUSCLES CAN BE ANGLED TO SPRAY TO LEFT OR RIGHT, LANDING WITH PINPOINT ACCURACY

---

is secreted by the anal glands, a pair of flask-shaped cavities flanking the animal's anus. Nearly all carnivores have these glands—they use the highly scented secretions for marking their territory—but in the skunks the glands are particularly large and productive. They are also highly modified for ballistic purposes, with each flask opening into a muscular nozzle like the barrel of a pistol. Small muscles aim the nozzles, and a layer of muscle surrounding the flask can be contracted to squirt the contents in a jet that may travel 22 ft (7 m) or more.

The scent fluid itself is an oily, yellow cocktail of sulfurous chemicals that has been compared to a

**WOLVES**

*are, next to humans, the wolverine's greatest enemy (above).*

*When it needs to defend itself, the wolverine can frighten off most intruders simply by bristling and snarling (below).*

Konrad Wothe/Oxford Scientific Films

mixture of garlic, rotten eggs, burning rubber, and singed hair. Although harmless to skin, the secretion is extremely painful if it gets into an animal's eyes, and it can even cause temporary blindness. So potent is the odor that it also inhibits breathing and leaves the victim choking helplessly. Skunks seem to know this; they always aim for the face. At ranges of 6 ft (2 m) or less they rarely miss. If the spray soaks into absorbent clothing, it is almost impossible to wash out, and the only sensible option is to burn it. The effect on hair and fur is almost as bad; if they have been sprayed once, few animals will risk a second strike.

## in SIGHT

### MUSCLE POWER

While the wolverine cannot match the skunks in the chemical defense league, it is quite capable of deterring its enemies in the same way. Its anal glands can spray a foul fluid, albeit somewhat haphazardly, up to 10 ft (3 m).

In practice, though, the wolverine rarely needs to use this defense. Few predators dare tangle with a wolverine, for, although relatively small, it is fearless and extremely strong. Except for humans, the only real threat to a wolverine is the wolf, a pack of which could rip it to shreds.

Renne Lynn/Photo Researchers/Oxford Scientific Films

Luckily for their neighbors, skunks are not too trigger-happy. Scent spraying wastes energy, and a skunk will give a potential enemy plenty of warning before opening fire. Often the mere sight of the patterned coat is enough to persuade a skunk-wise animal to stay well clear. A curious intruder, however, may alarm the skunk into a display designed to emphasize the color scheme and intimidate by a show of confidence. A striped skunk raises its bushy tail over its head, turns its hind end toward the threat, and stamps its forefeet menacingly. A spotted skunk will go further and kick its hind legs

*Upon meeting a ground squirrel, a striped skunk (above) fluffs up its tail in a mild show of strength; the squirrel will soon back off.*

**SPOTTED SKUNKS**
*have perfect aim— even from a handstand position (below).*

high in the air, "handstanding" for several seconds with its tail fluffed up. If this fails, it drops to all fours again, hisses at the threat, and displays its anal region. Finally, if all else fails, it sprays.

A skunk's accuracy is remarkable. Whatever the range, the two jets invariably converge on the target with devastating results. Dogs have been seen reeling back and retching in agony after a single blast, and a skunk is quite capable of spraying eight times in quick succession before it runs out of ammunition. Unfortunately for the skunk, however, some predators appear to be immune to the effects of the

EVEN THE FIERCEST OF PREDATORS WILL ABANDON A KILL AND FLEE RATHER THAN FACE UP TO A SKUNK

spray. Birds of prey in particular seem to ignore it, and a skunk's most dangerous enemy is the great horned owl, a powerful night hunter that occurs throughout the range of the various skunk species and has no hesitation in swooping down on a skunk and carrying it off in its talons, spray or no spray.

Despite the awesome stench it is capable of releasing, a skunk rarely smells "skunky" itself. Presumably the sheer power of its spray equipment is enough to propel the secretion well clear of its own fur. Occasionally rival skunks will spray one another, but only under extreme provocation. Skunks are obviously not immune to their own vile secretions, and they will generally avoid a confrontation that may escalate into a shooting match■

Illustrations John Cox/Wildlife Art Agency

# TERRITORY

Wherever they live, wolverines habitually range over huge areas. In Montana, for example, local wolverines each forage over an average of 150 sq miles (400 sq km) in winter, roaming some 25 miles (40 km) or more each night and resting up by day in a succession of temporary lairs. In Alaska, where food is harder to find, wolverines forage over 270 sq miles (700 sq km) or more, while on the Arctic tundra individual males have been known to range over an area of about 400 sq miles (1,000 sq km). Yet despite this apparent wanderlust, wolverines do not forage at random: Each individual wolverine revisits sites on a regular basis and reuses dens over and over again, although there may be an interval of several weeks between each visit. The animals are not true nomads; they simply have very extensive home ranges.

Many prey animals such as reindeer and ground-nesting birds migrate to the Arctic tundra in summer, and the wolverines living in the far north of the

---

**WITH THEIR BROAD PAWS, WOLVERINES CAN PATROL SEVERAL MILES OF SNOWY TERRITORY IN A SINGLE DAY**

---

taiga forest belt follow them. So an individual male wolverine with a winter range of, for example, 230 sq miles (600 sq km) in the taiga may move north in spring to a summer range of maybe 350 sq miles (900 sq km) on the open tundra, giving it a total range of some 580 sq miles (1,500 sq km)—a vast tract of land that could comfortably contain a large city.

Such an area cannot be defended effectively, but the wolverine certainly leaves its mark along its way to stake a claim of sorts. As it treks over tussock grassland, for example, it pauses periodically to straddle a grassy clump and smear scent on it. Its urine and droppings are also infused with its own personal scent, which informs neighboring wolverines of its identity, movements, gender, and sexual condition. It may also discourage an interloper from trespassing over the same terrain, simply because the alien scent saps the stranger's confidence and encourages it to return to familiar ground anointed with its own, reassuring scent.

Despite this the huge ranges of male wolverines overlap considerably, and the range of each male also includes the ranges of two or three females, which are generally much smaller. This is partly because females are themselves smaller: The body weight of an adult female is typically two-thirds that

***THE TERRITORIES*** *of male wolverines overlap in many cases, but confrontations are usually settled with a few wary snarls.*

of a male. But the smaller range of a female also reflects her possessive instincts, for whereas a male roams over a huge area, a breeding female defends a smaller area of some 20–135 sq miles (50–350 sq km) as her exclusive territory during the summer, liberally scent marking its border and driving out unwelcome trespassers. This secures a food supply for herself and her developing young at a time when she cannot move far from her home base. At the end of the breeding season, she starts foraging more extensively and becomes less interested in defending a well-defined territory.

# KEY FACTS

● Most wolverines defend a territory of some sort, although the defended area may be only a fraction of the total home range. In the state of Montana, however, neighboring wolverines seem to be unusually tolerant of each other, and territorial defense has never been observed. One theory is that their normal social reactions have been disrupted by the high death rate inflicted by relentless trapping.

● Although usually silent, the striped skunk is capable of producing a curious variety of sounds, including shrill screeches, low churring noises, and even birdlike twitters.

● Because the home ranges of wolverines are so vast, they live at comparatively low population densities. In northern Scandinavia an area of about 400 sq miles (1,000 sq km) may contain only two or three wolverines, so even in such unspoiled wilderness regions, the animals have always been scarce.

By wolverine standards, female skunks are almost sociable. Their food requirements are not great, since many live in areas where food is easy to come by—near human settlement, for example—so they can obtain everything they need within a home range of 0.4–0.8 sq miles (1–2 sq km). These

Erwin & Peggy Bauer/Bruce Coleman Ltd.

*Displaying her deadly dentition, a breeding female wolverine wards off intruders from her territory (above). Although small, these animals present such a furious defense that wolves, lynx, and even bears are stunned into retreating.*

wolverine, males occupy larger ranges encompassing those of several females, but they defend them resolutely against other males, intimidating rivals with threats and occasionally even spraying them. This rivalry has nothing to do with food resources; it simply stems from the male skunk's need to monopolize as many females as possible to maximize his lineage's chances for success. ∎

## *in* SIGHT

### SNUG LODGING

In Canada, where striped skunks enter a state of shallow hibernation in winter, a male will often secure his reproductive success by sharing a winter den with a group of females. Instead of patrolling the territories of several females in early spring to monitor their breeding condition, and risking being beaten to it by an intruding rival, he simply seeks out a group of females in late autumn and moves in with them, aggressively deterring other males from doing the same. Researchers in Alberta, for example, found that winter dens typically contained five or six females and a single male, comfortably placed to exploit his advantage in the spring.

Illustration Robin Budden/Wildlife Art Agency

ranges often overlap extensively with those of neighboring females. Outside the breeding season, several skunks may even share a den, particularly in the northern winter when the extra bodies cut down the loss of heat and energy.

The casual territoriality of female skunks is not shared by the males, however. As with the

# REPRODUCTION

Eero Murtomaki/NHPA

*Sparsely* distributed in their bleak northern habitats, roaming over vast tracts of forest and tundra, male and female wolverines rarely encounter one another and are often hostile when they do. Outside the breeding season, they may barely recognize a member of the opposite sex. As the pace of life quickens in April, however, an adult wolverine's instincts send it in search of a mate. The quest may be a long one, because the animals are so sparsely distributed. A male cannot simply go up to a female and court her favor; he must hope to pick up her scent and track her down. Luckily wolverines possess musk glands capable of laying an enticingly fragrant scent trail, rich with information about the animal's sexual status, so there is little risk of the male's being led astray.

---

**A SPRING BIRTH ENABLES THE MOTHER TO FIND FOOD NEAR THE NURSERY DEN; THIS IS ESSENTIAL, AS SHE CANNOT ROAM FAR**

---

Most matings occur from late April to July, but the implantation of the fertilized egg in the wall of the uterus is delayed by several weeks to extend the gestation to about nine months. By this means the birth of the young is postponed until the following spring, when food is beginning to become plentiful again after the rigors of winter. In normal circumstances, a mature female breeds every other year, but she may not breed at all after a poor feeding season; conversely, if food is particularly plentiful, female wolverines breed annually.

Two to four young, called kits, are born in a den dug into a deep snowdrift or nestled among boulders. Although fully furred at birth, they are helpless and do not open their eyes for three or four weeks. Their mother suckles them for about ten weeks,

and in that time she may change dens several times—either to avoid flooding by spring meltwater or as a precaution against human persecution.

The kits leave the den in early May, but they stay with the mother throughout the summer and autumn, sharing her prey and learning the arts of hunting and scavenging. During the winter the young males disperse, but the females may stay within their mother's home range indefinitely.

### MATING MADNESS

In skunks, the breeding season varies from region to region. Among spotted skunks, for example, the

*Mother and young share a reindeer carcass* (above).

**SKUNK KITS** *play under the watchful gaze of their mother* (right).

populations in the southeastern United States mate in March and April, and the young are born 50–65 days later. There is some delay in the implantation of the egg, but this amounts to only 14–16 days. By contrast, spotted skunks in the western states mate in September and October, but implantation is delayed until the following spring and the young are born from April to June. In both species the development of the embryo within the uterus, once implanted, takes only a month or so.

A male becomes much more active as the mating season approaches, extending his daily range and vigorously defending his territory (which

Janet Haas/Natural Science Photos

*Young skunks stay together until they are about five months old* (above).

encloses those of several females). According to some observers, he may also suffer a kind of "mating madness" that leads him to attack—and spray— animals of other species (including humans) that stray through his patch. The mating itself is often a rough affair, with the male chasing the female, grabbing her by the scruff of the neck and pulling her off her feet. Having mated, the two usually part for good. The male plays no part in raising his young, and indeed the female may have to defend them from aggression on his part.

The kits are born naked and blind, and their eyes open at twenty to thirty days. They are suckled for six to ten weeks, depending on the species. By the time they are weaned they can already use their spray defenses, and they will have accompanied their mother on a few hunting forays. The family unit remains together through the summer, but by early autumn the young skunks will have dispersed to acquire their own territories. ∎

Illustration John Morris/Wildlife Art Agency

## (in) SIGHT

### ROGUE MALES

A male wolverine can do little to benefit his kits, since the female supplies their every need. So his best chance of ensuring the survival of his line is to generate as many offspring as possible by mating with several females, a strategy typical of mustelids.

The males of some species monopolize groups of females within breeding territories. The striped skunk uses this tactic, but the wolverine cannot rely on it because the home ranges of the females are so large. Instead, he seems to mate promiscuously over a large area, hoping to "stake his claim" ahead of any nearby rivals.

# ON THE RUN FROM HUMANS

**ALTHOUGH IT INHABITS SOME OF THE MOST REMOTE HABITATS ON THE PLANET, THE WOLVERINE HAS NOT ESCAPED PERSECUTION BY HUMANS. ALWAYS SCARCE, IT MAY NOW BE SERIOUSLY RARE**

T he Arctic tundra and the great taiga forests that surround it are among the last untamed wildernesses on Earth. Shrouded in darkness for over half the year and chilled by the icy winds blowing off the polar ice cap, yet swarming with bloodsucking flies in summer, the whole region is one of the most inhospitable on the planet. Few people live there; agriculture is impossible, and in most areas the habitat has remained unchanged since the end of the last Ice Age over 10,000 years ago.

Accordingly this whole area has become a refuge for animals that have been all but eliminated in the more temperate latitudes. The larger carnivores in particular have been wiped out in many parts of Eurasia and North America, where they represented a threat to livestock and, in the imagination at least, to man himself. But cold-tolerant species, such as the gray wolf and the brown bear, still thrive in the remoter regions of the far north alongside strictly arctic species, such as the polar bear and Arctic fox. Their safety is not exactly guaranteed, but they are free from the persecution that has driven the southern races to the verge of extinction.

### AN INTERNATIONAL HIT LIST

The wolverine is not in the same league as the wolf or the bear, but it has suffered in much the same way. Within historical times it occurred as far south as northern Germany in Europe, and down to central California, southern Colorado, Indiana, and Pennsylvania in North America. But its lurid reputation for ferocity, coupled with its undoubted ability to kill and eat domestic livestock, made it an acceptable target, with the result that it has been eradicated from Europe, much of Scandinavia, and most of eastern and south-central Canada.

In the United States, widespread persecution throughout the last century reduced the species to a handful of remnant populations, notably in the mountains of Montana and northern California. These populations have subsequently increased, and since 1960 the wolverine has been reported from several states bordering the 49th Parallel. However, the animal remains extremely rare.

Today the main threat to the wolverine is hunting and trapping. A particularly long hunting season on the Kenai Peninsula—just south of Anchorage, Alaska—has been held responsible for the decline of the local wolverine subspecies to some 50 individuals, which is insufficient to guarantee its long-term survival. Populations in Sweden and Finland were reduced to similar levels in the 1960s, largely because the governments of these countries regarded the wolverine as a pest and paid a bounty for every dead animal. In 1973, it was estimated that only 40 wolverines survived in the wild in Finland, but despite this the Finnish government retained the bounty system until 1976.

Scandinavian hatred of the wolverine was—and is—fueled by its habit of preying on domestic reindeer. There is a long tradition of reindeer husbandry in Arctic Scandinavia, or Lapland, and until fairly recently the whole culture of the Lapps was based upon this animal. To these people the wolverine's notorious ability to overwhelm reindeer in deep snow qualified it as vermin, to be destroyed by whatever means possible.

Elsewhere, the criminal reputation of the wolverine is based mainly on its habit of stealing animals from traps. Fur trapping is still a flourishing business throughout the northern latitudes, despite the widespread development of fur farms and the reduced demand for furs by the fashion industry; and the wolverine is particularly

*A deadly bite for the skunk—and possibly for the wolf, since skunks are common carriers of rabies.*

Erwin & Peggy Bauer/Bruce Coleman Ltd.

*This chart shows the former and present range of the wolverine.*

**PRESENT RANGE**     **FORMER RANGE**

**Hunting and fur trapping once posed the biggest threats to the survival of the wolverine. Today it is the erosion of habitat in the more southerly part of its much-reduced range that could eventually cause the eradication of the species in all but the most remote and inhospitable of Arctic regions.**

adept at devouring the ensnared animals before they can be removed. Many of these are other mustelids—mink and sable, for example—but the wolverine is not fussy. To trappers a single sable represents a great deal of money, so many will shoot a wolverine on sight.

The wolverine is also valued as a furbearer itself. Alaska, for example, has yielded some 800 pelts annually in recent years—enough to make a substantial hole in the Alaskan wolverine population. The fur is not highly valued in general, but it is prized in the Arctic for lining hoods because it does not accumulate frost at the same rate as other furs. This is a major advantage in subzero temperatures, for otherwise the moisture in the wearer's breath tends to freeze onto the hood lining, thaw to a soggy mess on being brought inside, then freeze solid on reexposure.

So there are several reasons why a wolverine may run into a bullet if it is unlucky enough to come into contact with man. Yet only recently has it been

*A wolverine in northwest Canada gets caught in a trap. Its fur will be used for lining a hood.*

officially classified as being vulnerable over much of its range. In the far north, however, the sheer remoteness of its habitat may ensure its survival.

### UNWELCOME NEIGHBORS

Skunks also inhabit remote places, but in general they live in much closer contact with humans. Many species are found in highly populated, intensively farmed regions, and skunks frequently scavenge from garbage heaps in urban areas. Such behavior often indicates that the animals concerned have become acclimatized to the artificial environment to the point where they are able to exploit it for their own gain, but it does not mean that they are welcome. In the case of skunks, they are not.

Skunks are not exactly pests. In some ways they are even useful creatures; striped skunks, in particular, prey on rats and other vermin. Unlike the wolverine, they cannot be accused of killing and devouring domestic livestock, stealing valuable furbearing animals from traps, or being potentially dangerous to humans. Their unpopularity is based on their notorious chemical defenses and their role as carriers of a deadly disease—rabies.

As far as the chemical defenses are concerned, they work. Most people steer clear of skunks, and in general the animals are not greatly troubled by hunters. Skunk pelts do have some value, however, and at one time up to five million pelts were traded annually; most of these were obtained from striped skunks trapped in the north of their

**WOLVERINES & SKUNKS IN DANGER**

THE CHART BELOW SHOWS HOW THE INTERNATIONAL UNION FOR THE CONSERVATION OF NATURE (IUCN) CLASSIFIES THE STATUS OF THE WOLVERINE AND THE TEXAN SUBSPECIES OF THE SKUNK:

| | |
|---|---|
| WOLVERINES | VULNERABLE |
| BIG THICKET HOG-NOSED SKUNK | INDETERMINATE |

*VULNERABLE* INDICATES THAT THE ANIMAL IS LIKELY TO MOVE INTO THE ENDANGERED CATEGORY IF THINGS CONTINUE AS THEY ARE. *INDETERMINATE* MEANS THAT THE SPECIES IS ENDANGERED, VULNERABLE, OR RARE, BUT ITS PRECISE STATUS IS NOT FULLY KNOWN.

range, where the cold climate encourages a luxuriant growth of fur.

Today the market has contracted considerably, but some skunk species are still widely trapped for their fur. The decline of a Texan subspecies of the hog-nosed skunk to the point of near extinction has been attributed to fur trapping, as has the rarity of *Conepatus chinga rex*, a hog-nosed skunk found in northern Chile. The Patagonian hog-nosed skunk has also declined in numbers, partly as a result of trapping for its long, thick fur, but also because of habitat loss.

With these exceptions, however, skunks seem to flourish throughout the Americas. Like all wild animals, they are at risk from the destruction of the natural environment, but as adaptable opportunists they are better equipped than most to cope with a changing world. ■

*A rare sighting of a wolverine. Its notorious reputation has resulted in persecution by humans.*

# INTO THE FUTURE

The wolverine has never been a common animal. As a relatively large predator it is inevitably far less numerous than its prey. And since prey is generally scarce in the far north, where it lives, the wolverine has always been very scarce indeed. In Scandinavia a vast tract of land—maybe 780 square miles (2,000 square kilometers)—may contain up to ten wolverines, depending on the terrain, but rarely more. It is hardly surprising that the animal has remained so obscure.

Unfortunately, although this sparse distribution is perfectly natural, it makes the species particularly vulnerable to habitat destruction. If an area of wilderness is cut off by development of some kind—forestry, agriculture, or industry—a small, numerous species may barely notice the difference, but a wide-ranging, scarce species certainly will. Most important, its breeding options are restricted to the

## PREDICTION

### CREATURE OF THE WILDERNESS

*Although the wolverine is now protected from hunters and trappers throughout its range, it may not be long before it disappears entirely, simply through lack of space. If human activity wipes out the wilderness, it will also wipe out the wolverine.*

potential mates it still has access to, and, as we have seen, an isolated "island" of prime wolverine habitat may contain very few individual wolverines. The inevitable result is inbreeding, a decline in genetic variability, a possible decrease in fertility, and increased likelihood of local extinction.

Zoologists estimate that the "minimum viable population" necessary to prevent this is 500 individuals. As long as these 500 have free access to each other for breeding, the stock will remain healthy. If the population falls below 500 or is split by more development and isolation, it is doomed.

So what does this imply for the future? Simply that any isolated area of less than, say, 40,000 square miles (100,000 square kilometers) in the far north is unlikely to support a viable population. In Scandinavia and western Russia, the forest has been seriously eroded. Several species such as the sable have disappeared from Norway, Sweden, Finland, and western Russia, and the wolverine may not be able to hold out for much longer. ■

## SKUNKS AND RABIES

Rabies, or hydrophobia, is a viral disease of the central nervous system. Traditionally associated with mad dogs, rabies is also transmitted by several wild mammals. In North America it is widespread among foxes, raccoons, and skunks, and in recent years skunks seem to have become the main carriers.

Rabid skunks carry the virus in their saliva, and because the disease makes infected animals liable to attack and bite virtually anything that moves, the danger is very real. Skunks are considered to be the principal source of human infection in California and Texas, and since they often encounter domestic animals, the potential for transmission to other species is considerable.

The incidence of rabies cases often rises in the autumn and spring, when skunks—particularly males—tend to wander farther afield, carrying the virus with them.

Rabies is a lethal disease. The incubation period can last for many months, but the outcome is always fatal—to skunks as well as to other animals. A major outbreak can decimate a local skunk population, reducing contact between individuals and, therefore, reducing the chance of further infection. As a result, the disease tends to abate following an outbreak, only to reassert itself some three to four years later when the population has recovered.

## RUNNING OUT OF SPACE

*The wolverine is still found in the Stora Sjöfallet National Park in Sweden. But even Europe's largest preserve—2,000 sq miles (5,400 sq km) of tundra, taiga forest, and marshland—cannot support a viable population unless the animals can continue to move beyond the protected area to mate.*

Illustration Peter Bull

# WOLVES

G. Ziesler/Bruce Coleman Ltd.

*Wolves are carnivores, or meat-eaters. There are two types of carnivore—catlike forms and doglike forms. The doglike group is divided into four families, one of which is the canid or dog family and includes the wolves. This family is further broken down into ten genera (plural of genus) and thirty-five species. There are two wolf species.*

**ORDER**

*Carnivora*
(carnivores)

**SUPERFAMILY**

*Canoidea*
(doglike forms)

**FAMILY**

*Canidae* (dogs)

**GRAY WOLF GENUS**

*Canis*

**SPECIES**

*lupus*

**RED WOLF GENUS**

*Canis*

**SPECIES**

*rufus*

# THE TWILIGHT PROWLERS

## NOTORIOUS VILLAIN OF FABLE AND FAIRY TALE, THE WOLF IS A HIGHLY INTELLIGENT AND SOCIABLE ANIMAL WITH STRONG FAMILY BONDS

The wolf was once the most common, and also the most dreaded, wild animal of the northern lands. Its bad image is, however, an undeserved one. Shunned and feared by man for centuries, the wolf was commonly held to be an evil associate of the devil, partial to attacking and killing humans.

Nowadays, people are less inclined to believe in werewolves and the wolf's supernatural powers, but many still believe them to be man-eaters.

Discounting occasions in history when hungry wolves are said to have raided the aftermath of battlefields to eat human carrion, and the occasional attack by a rabid wolf deprived of its normal senses, nothing could be farther from the truth.

Wolves are very shy of humans and will go to great lengths to avoid them. Even naturalists who have spent years studying wolves have to work very hard to get close enough to study them properly.

A far cry from the evil, slavering, man-eating

2395

*The red wolf is smaller than the gray and is a highly endangered species found only in a small area of the southern United States.*

beast of legend, the wolf is one of the most intelligent and sociable of animals, living and hunting in a family-based pack. Surprisingly, all domestic dogs—from the German shepherd to the poodle—are descended from the wolf.

### EVOLUTIONARY HISTORY

The earliest ancestors of the wolf may have been members of a family called Miacoidea (mie-a-COY-dee-a), which lived during a prehistoric age called the Eocene period (54–38 million years ago). From their fossilized bones and teeth, experts believe that these early ancestors were tree-dwellers, with spreading paws and the distinctive

---

THE GRAY WOLF IS ABLE TO SURVIVE IN VERY COLD CLIMATES BECAUSE OF THE INSULATING QUALITIES OF ITS FUR

---

carnassial teeth. Two examples of these animals include Hesperocyon (hes-per-O-ky-on) in North America, and Cynodictis (kin-o-DIK-tiss) in Europe. With long bodies and short limbs, they resembled the modern civet (a member of the Feliform superfamily) in shape.

Toward the end of the Eocene period, and through the Oligocene and Miocene periods (38–7 million years ago), these early carnivores flourished, and adapted to the changes in climate, vegetation, and available prey. They eventually became ground-dwelling animals, and gradually the bone structure of their feet changed, helping them to run

## INTERBREEDING

The different species of dog of the genus *Canis*—wolf, coyote, dingo, jackal, and domestic dog—have the unusual ability to crossbreed successfully. In North America, coyotes, wolves, and domestic dogs occasionally interbreed to produce coy-wolf, coy-dog, and wolf-dog hybrids, which are fertile in both sexes. Because the species interbreed so readily, some of the rarer subspecies, such as the Apennine wolf in Italy, are in danger of disappearing.

Most experts now agree that all domestic dogs are descended from wolves, which were first tamed in the Near East (modern Iraq), 10,000–12,000 years ago.

Over thousands of years, many types of dogs have been bred from animals selected for special skills or qualities. One is the husky, a wolflike dog with a thick woolly coat, bred for strength to pull heavy loads across snowy terrain. Another is the marrema of Italy, which has been bred to look like a sheep, and lives with sheep flocks—guarding them against wolves!

Erwin & Peggy Bauer/Bruce Coleman Ltd.

*Gray wolf pup. Usually three to ten pups are born in an underground den excavated by the mother.*

faster after their prey over open ground. One of the earliest creatures recognizable as a wolf lived in the Pleistocene period (2 million years ago). Now known as the "Dire wolf," it was half as large again as the modern wolf.

### MODERN WOLVES

There are two species of wolf in existence today, the gray wolf and red wolf. The wolf's immediate family includes the dingo, coyote, jackal, and the familiar domestic dog. They all belong in turn to the wider dog family called Canidae (CANE-id-aye). Some of the wolf's relatives in this broad family include foxes and African wild dogs.

There are many similarities between the members of the dog family. All are adapted for hunting, with large pointed ears and sharp senses of hearing and smell to help them track down their prey. All have long legs and agile bodies that enable them to run in pursuit. Dogs have powerful jaws for crushing prey, and special teeth called "carnassials" for shearing through flesh. They have long tails with scent glands at the base for communication.

Unlike most dogs that readily eat whatever is available, including fruit and insects, the wolf is a dedicated carnivore, preferring a diet based almost entirely on meat. It lives and hunts as part of a highly organized team called a pack and has a complex social structure.

At first sight, the gray wolf bears a striking resemblance to the German shepherd dog. On closer inspection there are definite differences: The wolf's build is much stronger, its head is wider, the eyes more slanting, and the profile of the head shows a marked step between muzzle and crown. The wolf's physical features are perfectly suited to the tough life it leads in the wild.

The slender body and legs of the wolf give it the agility needed to chase its prey. From the long, pointed muzzle to the tip of the bushy tail, the wolf

---

**WOLVES LIVING IN COLD CLIMATES ARE GENERALLY BIGGER AND HEAVIER THAN THOSE OF WARMER CLIMATES**

---

is built for speed. Yet its build is strong, giving it stamina and enabling it to be a powerful attacker.

The fur of the wolf is dense, long, and soft, and they can survive in conditions of extreme cold and wet because of the special insulating quality of their fur. A dense layer of short, soft underfur grows next to the skin. This is kept dry by an outer layer of long "guard hairs," which repel water or snow before the underfur can get wet. Protected in this way, a wolf can sleep out on the open tundras of northern Canada in temperatures way below freezing, and travel through torrential rain if necessary.

Although the color of the coat varies, all wolves are paler on the underside with the upper parts sprinkled with black. A thick ruff of hair growing on the cheeks makes the head look larger than it actually is. When angry, the wolf erects a mane of long hairs on the back of the neck to make itself look even more threatening to a rival or an enemy. ∎

Illustrations Kim Thompson

# THE WOLVES' FAMILY TREE

*The family Canidae, known also as the canids, includes the jackal, dingo, coyote, and the domestic dog—all close relatives of the wolf. Other canids are the fox, raccoon dog, bush dog, maned wolf, dhole, and African wild dog. There are at least thirty-two subspecies of gray wolf. The red wolf is a separate species in the genus.*

## DOMESTIC DOG
*Canis familiaris*
*(ka-NIS fam-il-ee-AH-ris)*

### DINGO
*Canis dingo*
*(ka-NIS din-go)*

## COYOTE
*Canis latrans*
*(ka-NIS lat-rans)*

### JACKALS
*Four species in the genus* Canis

## FOXES
*Twenty-one species in four genera*

# GRAY WOLF

*Canis lupus (ka-NIS LOO-puss)*

The gray wolf is also called the timber wolf or the white wolf. Over thirty different subspecies have been recorded. The common wolf is medium-sized with short, dark fur. It lives in the forests of Europe and Asia. The Steppe wolf is smaller and has a grayish brown coat. It lives in the grasslands (steppes) of central Asia. Tundra wolves have pale coats to blend in with the habitat while Arctic wolves are often white. The eastern timber wolf is the most widespread variety in North America and has gray fur. Farther south, the rare Mexican wolf is smaller and darker. Arabian and Tibetan subspecies have also been identified.

# RED WOLF

*Canis rufus (ka-NIS ROO-fuss)*

The red wolf is smaller than the gray wolf. Once thought to be extinct in its native forest or coastal plains habitats in southeast United States, it has now been successfully reintroduced to the wild where its progress is being monitored.

## WILD DOGS

*Five species in five genera*

ALL DOGS

# ANATOMY:
## THE WOLF

The gray wolf is larger than the red wolf and considerably larger than most domestic dogs. Its nearest domestic likeness is the German shepherd dog.

The wolf's limbs are long, with four toes on the hind foot and five on the forefoot. The claws, which are used for digging when burying food, are large and do not retract like a cat's. They are clearly visible in the wolf's footprint.

### HEARING

With its large, pointed ears, the wolf is able to hear very faint sounds made by prey from a considerable distance—the equivalent of being able to hear a watch ticking 33 ft (10 m) away. The wolf relies on its hearing for hunting, much more than on its eyesight, which is not particularly good.

### SENSE OF SMELL

All dogs are noted for their acute sense of smell, which has been put to good use by humans—German shepherd dogs are trained to sniff out drugs and explosives, for example. The wolf is no exception and relies heavily on its sense of smell for tracking prey and recognizing other wolves and their territory.

### WALKING/RUNNING

Wolves walk with a trotting pace and leave a single line of paw prints. Other wolves walk along the leader's tracks in single file. Wolves are good runners and, with their great stamina, can keep up their loping style of running over long distances, managing speeds of up to 28 mph (45 km/h) in shorter bursts.

Color illustrations Guy Troughton/Wildife Art Agency

The skeleton of the wolf is well adapted to its lifestyle. The bones need to be strong, for power in bringing down large prey such as caribou or moose. The narrow collarbones, interlocked foreleg bones, and specially adapted wrist bones give the wolf streamlining, strength, and speed.

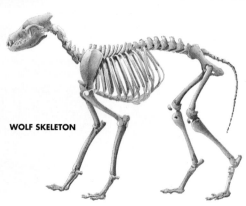

**WOLF SKELETON**

The wrist bones of the wolf are fused together for extra strength. When closed, the toes are rugged and strong. Splaying the toes allows the wolf to grip on to slippery, uneven, and steep surfaces.

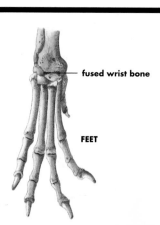

fused wrist bone

**FEET**

X-ray illustrations Elisabeth Smith

The broad head and long muzzle of the wolf contain strong jaws and teeth. The pointed canine teeth can be up to 2 in (5 cm) long. Powerful face muscles hold the teeth locked together and help the wolf hang on to its prey.

## STREAMLINED SHAPE

The wolf is built for speed as it travels in pursuit of prey, often under cover through dense woodland and undergrowth: pointed muzzle, head, and ears; narrow chest; long, slim legs; smooth fur; slender, tapering body; and long, pointed tail.

## FUR

Soft, thick underfur keeps the wolf warm and dry, and long "guard" hairs keep snow and water out. Pale underparts, blotchy darker markings on the body, ears, and tail, and color to match habitat, give the wolf the advantage of camouflage as it moves up on its prey.

An open mouth reveals the contents of the long muzzle—a set of 42 fearsome-looking teeth made up of 6 incisors, 2 canines, 8 premolars, and 6 molars in the lower jaw. The upper jaw has 2 fewer molars.

The elongated shape of the skull is typical of the dog family.

WOLF SKULL
(side view)

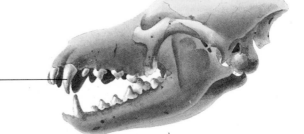

canine teeth

# PACK HUNTERS

WOLVES ARE THE BIG GAME HUNTERS OF THE DOG FAMILY. THEY OWE
THEIR SUCCESS TO THEIR STRATEGY OF HUNTING AS A TEAM. EVEN
WHEN HUNTING ALONE, A SINGLE WOLF CAN OVERPOWER A DEER

Wolves are the most social species of the dog family, living in highly organized packs and hunting together as a team. Recent observations by naturalists have revealed that the wolf is an appealing, interesting creature of great integrity, intelligence, and friendliness. The social structure of the pack is fundamentally a guarantee of food, relying on the principle that cooperation endows certain advantages to each individual.

Pack members are loyal and will fiercely protect their territory from neighboring packs. They are playful and curious (not only on the part of the cubs) and display considerable family feeling: The breeding pair mate for life, and all pack members share in the care and education of the young.

Wolves show obvious delight when they recognize

**WOLVES OFTEN TRAVEL LONG DISTANCES IN SEARCH OF FOOD. TO TRAVEL 30 MILES (48 KM) IN A DAY IS NOT UNUSUAL**

their fellow pack members and seem to enjoy doing things together, such as an enthusiastic "group howl," which involves every pack member, right down to the cubs.

Wolves are individuals too, each one having its own distinctive smell, voice, and particular hunting skills. They deliberately leave scent marks wherever they go by urinating in prominent places, such as on rocks or trees. Other wolves can read these scent marks to discover who has passed before, their sex and status, and whether they belong to the same or different pack.

Yet wolves remain fiercely wild and tough, and there is little room for sentimentality. Old or sick pack members are made outcasts when they have outlived their usefulness. Members of rival packs

are treated ruthlessly, and wolves will kill almost any prey worth eating. This contrast in behavior makes the wolf an interesting animal to study.

The wolf has considerable physical strength—a single full-grown wolf can bring down and kill a large steer. It also has great stamina and impressive powers of endurance. Compared with the cheetah, which can reach 60 miles (96 kilometers) per hour over short distances, the wolf is not a fast runner. It runs at about 24 miles (38 kilometers) per hour, and can reach 28 miles (45 kilometers) per hour for short distances to close in on its prey.

Though not a sprinter, the wolf is a good marathon runner—it can keep up a steady loping run for many hours and, because of its great stamina, it can outrun most large game animals.

The wolf is also a fine swimmer and will not hesitate to follow deer into the water if there is the chance of a kill. ■

Tom Brakefield

ZEFA

## DISTRIBUTION

*The laid-back ears of the two wolves (far left) mean aggression. A change in leadership often results in skirmishes within the pack.*

*Most of the wolf's food is caught on the run. Once stopped, the entire pack joins in the kill, which usually takes a few minutes.*

# HABITATS

The gray wolf is an animal of the northern hemisphere and is found north of the latitude 20°N. It was once widespread over Europe (including the British Isles), most of Asia, and North America. An extremely adaptable animal, it can thrive in a wide variety of habitats, from semidesert to Arctic.

The wolf's body is well equipped to cope with extremes of temperature and rainfall and a wide variety of terrain and vegetation. It can always survive as long as there is an adequate supply of fresh meat and a reasonable amount of cover.

The wolf's coat color is often matched to habitat, which gives it the benefit of camouflage in

## KEY FACTS

● One of the largest packs ever recorded had thirty-six wolves, and was in Alaska.

● Wolf howls normally carry up to 5–6 miles (8–10 km) in open country, though humans have been able to hear howls from 10 miles (16 km) away.

● A pack howling bout can be heard over an area of 116 sq mi.

● Wolves eat 11–22 lb (5–10 kg) of meat a day.

● A pack in Alaska traveled 700 miles (1,126 km) in forty two days.

hunting its prey and escaping the attention of its enemies or rivals.

The wolves of the sunbaked semidesert and rocky scrublands may be pale and sandy colored. Wolves of shady forests tend to be gray, while the fur of tundra and Arctic wolves may change from white in winter to gray in summer when the snow melts over the cold northern wastes.

Wolves are perhaps most at home in the great forests of North America and Europe. Here, they merge into the shadows in deep pine forests and mixed deciduous woodland. There is no shortage of cover and a plentiful supply of game such as deer, moose, and elk. Winters are long and cold and summers short and mild, but the wolf finds plenty of protection in the often mountainous landscape.

In Europe, wolves are found in the high forests of Cantabria and Galicia in Spain and the remote woods of Portugal. Romania has a decent-sized population and wolves are also found in several other European countries.

In more southerly latitudes, wolves may have to contend with excessive heat rather than cold, although nights in the semidesert climate can be surprisingly cold.

Around the Mediterranean, wolves survive in

## FOCUS ON

### THE CANADIAN ARCTIC

In the Arctic and tundra regions of northern Canada, Alaska, Scandinavia, and Siberia, the winters are long and cold. Rainfall is light, but tends to fall as snow. In the cutting winds and thin soil, little grows except lichens and shallow-rooted, low-growing plants.

It is here that the wolf relies on rocks and caves for cover. Long, thick fur protects the wolf from extreme cold—temperatures may be as low as -50°F (-46°C)—and its pale or white color camouflages it well when it is hunting.

During severe weather the wolf depends on smaller mammals such as Arctic hares and lemmings for food. But, like other rodents, lemming numbers fluctuate wildly from season to season, and sometimes the population crashes completely. In these years the winter claims many wolf casualties.

---

## DAYLIGHT HOURS

Illustration Paul Williams

**DAYLIGHT HOURS AT:**

☐ 60° NORTH

☐ 70° NORTH

*In the Arctic summer, which lasts from July to August, the sun never sets, and in the depths of winter, in December and January, it does not rise.*

| Month | 60° NORTH | 70° NORTH |
|---|---|---|
| JAN | 6.38 | 0 |
| FEB | 9.11 | 7.20 |
| MAR | 11.41 | 11.28 |
| APR | 14.31 | 16.06 |
| MAY | 17.04 | 22.13 |
| JUN | 18.49 | 24 |
| JUL | 17.31 | 24 |
| AUG | 15.46 | 18.26 |
| SEP | 13.00 | 13.34 |
| OCT | 10.11 | 9.03 |
| NOV | 7.37 | 3.06 |
| DEC | 5.54 | 0 |

---

mountain refuges in Greece and former Yugoslavia. In the deserts and semideserts of Iran, Arabia, Egypt, and Mexico, wolves tend to have short, pale, or sandy colored coats. Cover is provided by rocks and caves in the barren mountain ridges, where the animals sometimes have to rely on small prey.

Although the wolf has few natural enemies, it does not always exist peacefully alongside other predators, such as the coyote, which compete for the same prey, and it will defend its territory from such intruders. ∎

### NEIGHBORS

Regarded as the true home of the wolf, North America supports a rich diversity of wildlife and habitats and the wolf can adapt to most of them, including the inhospitable tundra.

**BALD EAGLE**

Feeding mainly on fish, this large bird of prey also hunts rabbits, squirrels, waterfowl, and rats.

**SOCKEYE SALMON**

Unlike the Pacific and Atlantic salmon, the sockeye lives and spawns in landlocked freshwater.

Illustrations Chris Christoforou

ENEMIES

**EXTREMLEY DANGEROUS**

### GRIZZLY BEAR
*The powerful grizzly is very aggressive and any animal that threatens it will be charged and possibly killed.*

**MODERATELY DANGEROUS**

### BISON
*Although wolves hunt bison, they are very careful around a healthy adult. One kick can crush the ribs of a wolf.*

### RANGE OF ARCTIC WOLF
*The Arctic wolf lives in one of the most inhospitible places on earth where temperatures remain below zero for much of the year. Here the wolf eats what it can, often small mammals such as Arctic hares and lemmings.*

■ NORTH AMERICAN RANGE OF ARCTIC WOLF

**BOBCAT**

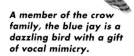

The reddish brown coat of the bobcat offers wonderful camouflage against the dense terrain it inhabits.

**BLUE JAY**

A member of the crow family, the blue jay is a dazzling bird with a gift of vocal mimicry.

**2-SPOT LADYBUG**

The bright coloration of this insect warns potential predators to leave it alone. Ladybugs feed on aphids.

**PORCUPINE**

The spines and quills of the porcupine are really modified hairs. The spines are solid; quills are hollow.

**TREEHOPPER**

The treehopper has an enlarged shield over its thorax and back that looks like a sharp thorn.

# SOCIAL STRUCTURE

Wolves are social creatures that usually live and hunt together in packs. The primary purpose of the pack is to hunt for food more efficiently. In the same way that human beings work together for a particular aim, the wolves pool their skills and strength to work as a team for the benefit of the social unit as a whole.

Generally speaking, the larger their local prey, the larger the packs tend to be. The average size of the pack can vary from anything between two to twenty-five animals. Though the average is five or six, packs numbering as many as thirty-six individuals have been recorded in Alaska. At the other extreme, single pairs are quite common.

### SOCIAL HIERARCHY

The pack has a definite social structure with each wolf allotted a specific role to play and with its own particular place in the hierarchy. A large, well-established pack is led by a top male and female, known as the "alpha" pair. These adult wolves form the only breeding pair in the pack and are frequently the parents of the other pack members.

The second-ranked male and female are known as the "beta" wolves. These, along with the other adult members of the pack, do not breed. At the bottom of the pack hierarchy are the subadult animals and members with less than perfect health.

Most of the adults, and some of the immature wolves, take part in hunting. Others may remain behind to look after the younger pups as "helpers."

### HARMONY

*Wolves stay relaxed as younger members of the pack play-fight and jostle for status. Each wolf knows its place in the hierarchy and serious conflicts are rare.*

When there are no major changes in the supply of food, packs tend to remain fairly stable in size and structure from year to year. The alpha male and female usually pair for life, though a constant trickle of younger wolves leave to start their own packs.

### CONFRONTATIONS

The order of ranking within the pack is often challenged. Although wolves rarely fight to inflict wounds, they use a variety of expressions and body postures in "ritual confrontations"—fights acted out according to set patterns.

Higher-ranked wolves will confirm their position by raising the tail, standing stiff-legged, baring their teeth aggressively, and shoving the weaker animal. Lower-ranked pack members accept their position with submissive gestures such as lowering the head, flattening the ears, and dropping the tail between the legs.

Often these gestures recall

Udo Hirsch/Bruce Coleman Ltd.

*A low-status wolf (left) cringes submissively in response to a threat. Such gestures help to keep the peace within the pack.*

the behavior of pups, for example rolling over and exposing the belly, or licking the superior wolf's mouth as if begging for food. By these actions the submissive wolf seems to be trying to remove the threat by bringing out parental feelings in the dominant wolf. These ritual confrontations confirm the pack leadership and preserve the peace.

Wolves are generally very affectionate toward other pack members. They greet each other with excited tail-wagging and face-licking. The alpha male is rarely aggressive with the members of his pack and can actually be quite tolerant of them, as if encouraging them and keeping up their morale.

### EXPRESSIONS, SCENTS, AND SOUNDS

Wolves have very expressive faces and can show their feelings by gestures of the forehead, mouth, ears, and eyes. For example, if a wolf is afraid or insecure, it keeps its teeth covered, pulls the corners of its mouth back in a smilelike submissive "grin," narrows its eyes to slits, smooths its forehead, and flattens its ears against its head.

A confident, threatening expression is just the reverse: bared teeth, mouth corners forward, wrinkled muzzle, frowning forehead, and erect, forward-pointing ears. A direct stare will also be interpreted as aggressive, while a wolf that is trying to pacify another will look away from it.

Wolves also communicate by smell. Leaving scent marks of urine, they can inform other wolves of territorial boundaries and provide information about their sex, status, and movements.

Close together, wolves use a variety of noises —whimpers, whines, squeaks, yelps, barks, snarls, and growls. For long-distance communication, wolves howl, either to locate fellow pack members, or to advertise their presence to neighboring wolf packs. ∎

**SIGN LANGUAGE**
*The subtle interactions between wolves are often invisible to outsiders.*

### EXPRESSIONS

**Bared teeth, erect ears, and staring eyes are signs of a strong dominance threat.**

**A wolf under threat may flatten its ears and hide its teeth to indicate fear or submission.**

**Pricked-up ears indicate confidence, but the tight-lipped "grin" shows that the wolf is not sure of itself.**

**A protruding tongue may be a gesture of submission, but here the erect ears indicate hostility.**

Illustrations Simon Turvey

## AMAZING FACTS

### LONE WOLF

Not all wolves live as part of a pack. A "lone wolf" is usually a young animal that has left to find a mate and a place to start a pack of its own, but some are old or sick animals that have become outcasts.

Lone wolves travel over areas ten to twenty times greater than a pack. They keep a low profile, rarely howling or scent marking until they claim their own territory.

Life is dangerous for the lone wolf. Deprived of the protection of the pack, many do not survive long.

# HUNTING

olves will hunt almost anything that moves, but they prefer to prey on larger beasts such as musk ox, moose, caribou, deer, elk, and reindeer. Large prey are available only in certain habitats and, even there, wild populations may be much reduced due to human activities. Wolves will then turn their attention to domestic livestock such as horses, cattle, sheep, and goats.

They will occasionally eat wild boars, beavers, dogs, hares, birds, and carrion, and they will make do with mice, voles, frogs, and almost any other small animal, which they sniff out in the grass and pounce on with their paws. If desperate, wolves will even eat potatoes and fruit such as figs, blackberries, and grapes.

Where food is scarce, the normally shy wolf will venture to the edges of human settlements to scavenge garbage cans and refuse dumps at night. On the barren tundra, a hungry wolf may eat buds and lichens until it can find meat again.

Throughout their range wolves are shy and secretive animals, preferring to remain hidden

**SIGHT**

Martin W. Grosnick/Ardea

## WOLFING ITS FOOD

**Most wolf hunts end in failure, and an individual wolf may have to go several days without eating. So when it does make a kill, a wolf makes the most of the opportunity and may gorge itself on up to 20 lb (9 kg) of meat at a sitting. Not content with that, it will often carry off some of the meat and bury it for later before settling down to digest its meal.**

### GROUP HOWLING

*The pack will often gather for a group howl before setting out on a hunt. The pack starts its journey walking in single file behind the alpha male.*

and to move unseen. Their sharp senses help them track prey quietly and stealthily.

Wolves often travel and hunt at night, so perhaps it is not surprising that they do not rely to any great extent on their eyesight to follow prey. Their eyesight is actually quite poor. Their yellowish eyes do not glow in the dark, as many horror films have portrayed them, but simply reflect small quantities of light, like the eyes of many other animals.

Wolves rely much more heavily on their superb hearing and sense of smell. They are able to hear very slight sounds over long distances, for example, a snapping twig up to 2 miles (3 kilometers) away. They also hear a much wider range of pitch than the human ear can detect.

Their sense of smell is even sharper—a wolf can recognize hundreds of thousands of smells that humans cannot detect or distinguish. Constantly bombarded with a stream of different scents, the wolf can take advantage of what is practically an extra dimension. It can smell a moose from a distance of 1.2 miles (2 kilometers).

By "reading" scents, the wolf obtains vital information on the type, condition, and movements of the animal it is tracking. It remembers and recognizes the smells and scents of landmarks to build up a "mental map" of the terrain.

Where larger prey is available, wolves hunt in

## PREY

*Wolves prefer to take large prey such as moose and caribou, hunting as a pack, but an individual wolf will often feed on smaller animals such as hares, mice, and frogs.*

MOOSE

CARIBOU

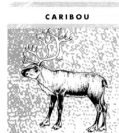

All illustrations John Cox/Wildlife Art Agency

packs, spending most of their time in search of food. The pack gathers and, perhaps after a "group howl," sets out into the depths of its territory, walking in single file. On the way, burrows may be investigated for any edible occupants, and any found to be empty are scent-marked so that no time will be wasted on a future hunt.

Eventually the scent of prey is picked up, sometimes from a distance of a few miles, at which point the wolves gradually work their way toward the target, hunting as a team. Some crouch and stalk slowly, another may act as a decoy while the rest move up for a surprise attack.

### TEAMWORK
*When they tackle large prey, the pack must hunt as a team to have any chance of success.*

Others that are powerful runners move in once the prey has started to move. Sometimes one or two wolves run on ahead out of sight of the prey, to cut off possible escape routes. Often the pack will single out a weak or young individual, scattering the herd to separate the target animal.

Once the chase is on, it can stretch over a great many miles until the prey tires and a wolf can reach it. Often the prey is first bitten in the rear, and eventually bitten in the neck or head to kill it.

Wolves do not always manage to kill their prey. For every kill, nine other hunts are unsuccessful. Often the pack will give up the chase if the target animal turns out to be a dangerous individual. Large animals such as moose can inflict terrible wounds with their antlers, and the wolf prefers to go hungry rather than take too great a risk.

When a kill is made, the wolves feed quickly, eating bones, skin, and fur along with the flesh. They hurry back to the den to feed the cubs with fresh or regurgitated meat, then lie under cover to digest their meal. ■

### CLOSING IN
*One wolf heads off the prey while the others bring it down.*

| BEAVER | GOAT | DOMESTIC DOG | MUSTANG | DALL SHEEP | SNOW HARE |
|--------|------|--------------|---------|------------|-----------|

# TERRITORY

Each wolf pack establishes its own separate territory, an area of land that contains its den and where it hunts for food. The size of a territory depends on the amount of available prey, and can vary from 40 square miles (104 square kilometers) to over 400 square miles (1,036 square kilometers) in areas where prey is very scattered.

The boundaries of a territory may change during the year. On the open tundra of North America, wolves migrate over hundreds of miles, following their prey of caribou and saiga antelope. In forests and on islands, the shapes of territories are more clearly defined by natural boundaries and are stable throughout the year.

## A WELL-DEFINED TERRITORY IS VITAL TO PACK SURVIVAL, SINCE IT PROVIDES BOTH FOOD AND SECURITY

However far they travel in search of food, adult wolves will eventually return to an established rendezvous site at the heart of their territory. This is a den situated above ground that serves as the pack's headquarters. Young pups are left here for protection, often guarded by adults.

Like dogs, wolves mark the boundaries of their territory by spraying permanent objects that are situated along the borders. Bushes, tree trunks, logs, rocks, clumps of grass, and chunks of ice are all sprayed with urine and scent from a gland under the tail. Sometimes the line of a natural boundary, such as a river, may form the border of a territory.

Illustration Simon Turvey

Trails and crossroads are frequently marked. Most of the marking is done by the alpha male, but other members of the pack will add their marks to his. Sometimes a whole line of wolves will wait their turn to leave their scent on a favorite mark.

Wolves from neighboring packs also pick up information from these scent marks, such as how many wolves have been there and how recently. They will in turn scent mark their side of the territorial boundary. Often a "no go" area exists between territories, about half a mile wide, which all the wolves will normally avoid. When times of food shortage force them to hunt in these border areas, they risk meeting wolves from neighboring packs. If a wolf strays and meets another pack, it may be attacked and even killed.

Wolves become very familiar with the layout of their own territory by scent marking special places such as kill sites and trail junctions, so that they become recognizable landmarks. Those who study

### PACK DISPUTES

*The territories of neighboring wolf packs often overlap at places where prey animals congregate in winter, and violent encounters between packs become more common during the winter months.*

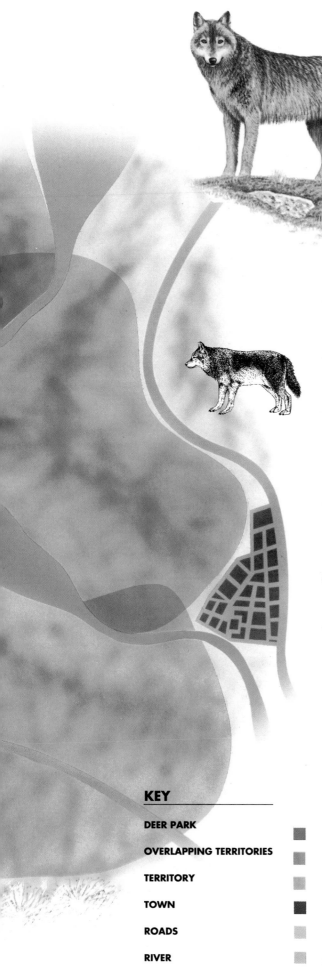

wolves have reported that within the home territory wolves do not wander aimlessly about, but tend to use favorite routes, hunting trails, lookout positions, kill sites, and resting places, as well as a particular denning area.

If a wolf picks up the scent mark of a "foreigner" in its territory, it will "overmark" with its own scent to underline its warning to the intruder. Wolves increase their rate of scent marking after coming across a stranger's scent. This leads to a greater concentration of scent marks at border areas and helps to emphasize the territorial borders for future recognition.

---

### SILENT STALKER

*A lone wolf must keep a low profile when crossing pack territory, and it usually keeps to neutral ground.*

### SCAVENGERS

*Wolf territories rarely encompass human settlements, although hungry wolves may enter towns to scavenge rubbish dumps.*

---

**IN SOME AREAS, FIGHTING BETWEEN NEIGHBORING PACKS IS THE MAIN CAUSE OF DEATH AMONG ADULT WOLVES**

---

Wolves like to howl together as a pack, to let other packs know that they are close. Neighboring packs will usually howl back in response, in defense of their own territory.

Occasionally an outside pack will deliberately ignore warnings and invade a neighboring territory. They will make for the pack's resting place and attack, kill, and scatter members of the resident pack to take over their territory. Normally, however, the territorial system works well, insuring that most wolf packs live side by side in relative peace. ■

## WHY DO WOLVES HOWL?

**Howling is a means of long-distance communication, used to contact pack members far out in the territory or to warn neighboring packs of their presence. All wolves howl with a slightly different note, and wolves may be able to recognize the howl of each individual.**

**Wolves may also howl because they enjoy it. A group howl often occurs before a hunt, and all the wolves are eager to join in. Group howling seems to strengthen family bonds and loyalty to the pack.**

A. & S. Carey/Oxford Scientific Films

## KEY

DEER PARK

OVERLAPPING TERRITORIES

TERRITORY

TOWN

ROADS

RIVER

# LIFE CYCLE

In wolf packs, mating is limited to one breeding pair—usually the alpha male and female—although in smaller packs there may only be one pair mature enough to breed anyway.

During a four-week period in the spring, all the adult females in the pack are able to mate so the alpha pair assert their breeding rights over the rest of the group. The alpha female will aggressively force the other females temporarily from the pack.

---

**ALTHOUGH THERE IS ONLY ONE BREEDING PAIR IN THE PACK, ALL THE ADULTS HELP REAR THE PUPS**

---

Tensions run high as the alpha male dominates the other males to prevent them from mating with her. Eventually the alpha pair mate, and peace returns to the pack.

The male wolf's penis contains a bony structure called the "baculum." After mating, the male and female turn to face in opposite directions, but this has the effect of locking the two animals together for up to a half hour or more. They remain like this until the blood vessels trapped in the swollen baculum can return to normal. No one knows for certain why this happens, although it may help to create a "pair-bond" between the male and female.

After about six weeks, the pregnant female will prepare a den for the pups. In the late spring, after a gestation period of sixty-three days, she settles alone there to give birth to a litter, typically of five or six pups. The newborn pups are blind, deaf, and helpless and can do little but wriggle and squirm and suck their mother's milk.

## FROM BIRTH TO DEATH

**GRAY WOLF**

| | |
|---|---|
| **GESTATION:** 63 DAYS | ESTABLISHED AT 12 WEEKS |
| **LITTER SIZE:** 5–6 PUPS | **FOLLOW THE PACK:** 3–5 MONTHS |
| **WEIGHT AT BIRTH:** 1 LB (450 G) | **INDEPENDENCE:** 10 MONTHS |
| **EYES OPEN:** 2–3 WEEKS | **FULLY GROWN:** 18 MONTHS |
| **FIRST WALKING:** 3 WEEKS | **SEXUAL MATURITY:** 2 YEARS |
| **WEANED:** 7–8 WEEKS | (FEMALE); 3 YEARS (MALE) |
| **LEAVE DEN:** 8–10 WEEKS | **LONGEVITY IN WILD:** 15–16 YEARS |
| **HIERARCHY:** TOP PUP | (UP TO 20 YEARS IN CAPTIVITY) |

**RED WOLF**

ALTHOUGH THE RED WOLF IS SMALLER AND LIGHTER THAN THE GRAY WOLF, THE LIFE CYCLE DETAILS ARE THE SAME.

**CONCEPTION**

*The parent wolves mate in the spring, after several days of tension within the pack.*

**INPEPENDENCE**

*Eventually the young wolves leave the pack to mate and claim territories of their own.*

**ADOLESCENCE**

*As they grow the young wolves learn to assert themselves, laying the foundations for their future role in the pack.*

# GROWING UP

*The life of a young wolf*

### BIRTH

*Blind, deaf, and helpless, the pups are born in a secure den in the heart of the pack territory.*

### INFANCY

*At first the pups rely on their mother's milk, and depend on her to keep them safe from other predators.*

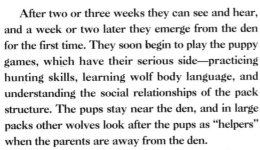

After two or three weeks they can see and hear, and a week or two later they emerge from the den for the first time. They soon begin to play the puppy games, which have their serious side—practicing hunting skills, learning wolf body language, and understanding the social relationships of the pack structure. The pups stay near the den, and in large packs other wolves look after the pups as "helpers" when the parents are away from the den.

Soon the pups are too big for the den and the family moves to a "rendezvous site" for the rest of the summer. This is an area of about half an acre (1,000 square meters) where the pups can play safely, and to which the adults return every day.

## WOLVES' DEN

A. Wolfe/ZEFA

**A typical wolf den is made by a pregnant female in a sandy hillside where the ground is easy to dig and well-drained. It is usually close to a supply of drinking water from a spring, river, or lake. The pregnant wolf sometimes adapts an old porcupine den or badger sett, digging under tree roots or rocks for extra protection. In the Arctic, the wolf den is often a protected hollow in the ground.**

**The burrow is usually about 16 in (40 cm) high and 26 in (65 cm) wide. Inside, 6 ft (1.8 m) from the burrow entrance is a sharp turn with a rounded hollow where the mother sleeps. The burrow then slants slightly upward for about 6 ft (1.8 m), to a snug chamber where the pups stay until they begin venturing out after four or five weeks.**

At ten months the pups join in hunting, acting as observers on their first few expeditions. At eighteen months, they are adult size. When they reach sexual maturity in their second year, some will leave the pack and travel as lone wolves until they find a mate. Males often remain in the pack longer than their sisters.

A wolf can live for nine to ten years if it survives the threat of human hunters, starvation, or aggression from other wolf packs; though as it reaches old age, its teeth become worn, and it is a less efficient hunter.

Sometimes an old wolf is fed and protected by the younger pack members, who rely on its experience of territory and prey. Old and sick animals may, however, be treated as outcasts of the pack when they have outlived their usefulness. ■

# HUNTER OR HUNTED?

## WOLVES HAVE ALWAYS LIVED ALONGSIDE HUMANS SHARING FOOD AND FOREST ALIKE, BUT HAS THE NEED FOR FARMLAND AND HOUSES LEFT ANY ROOM FOR THE WOLF?

For centuries wolves have been part of human legend and culture. They have been feared—and respected—as fierce, strong hunters. Because of our fear of them—and because they kill and eat livestock—they have been persecuted, with more and more of their forest habitat cleared away to make room for farms and settlements.

Today the wolf is in an unusual position: While some people still persecute it, others work hard to save it. A growing number of people, especially in North America, see the wolf and its howls as the perfect symbol of wilderness.

However, in many other cultures the fear of wolves taking livestock is a real one. It is said that a pack of wolves can kill scores of sheep in a night, and in the past this must have filled farmers with terror. Loss of livestock was quite literally a matter of life and death for the medieval farmer.

### UNFOUNDED FEARS

At the same time, the threats to human life are exaggerated. Shepherds in Greece carry nothing but staffs to protect themselves and their flocks. The shepherd has only to shake his staff at wolves and they will flee.

There are very few authenticated cases of people being killed by wolves, and in many of the known cases the animals concerned were rabid. But this has never prevented the fear of wolves being used as an excuse for killing them. They have also been hunted for their coats, which are thick and warm—a useful commodity in the cold climates of prime wolf habitat.

The wolf's natural range, which stretched right across the northern hemisphere, was once the greatest of any land animal. Today, of course, it is much reduced, and very different animals have taken over the mantle of being the most widespread: rats, cockroaches, and feral pigeons, for example. Even so, the wolf's great natural range has helped it to survive in a number of places where wilderness remains, even though it has been exterminated in others.

The wolf is still common only in the great wild conifer woods of the far north, in Canada and Siberia. Estimates suggest there may be more than 50,000 wolves in North America, primarily in Canada and Alaska.

In other areas it has long gone. The last Irish wolf lived around 1770, wolves were wiped out in Scotland by 1740, and in England and Wales by 1500. In other places it hangs on in perilously small numbers—there are thought to be no more than fourteen surviving in Norway and Sweden combined. This

A. Wolfe/ZEFA

Frank Spooner Pictures

*This wolf, like many others, was shot during a very cold period in Turkey when it moved into the town in search of food.*

*When living close to humans, wolves will steal livestock if it is not well protected.*

is tragic for the wolf in Scandinavia, for these countries have small populations per square mile and large numbers of prey animals. Yet, as soon as the wolf numbers increase, the locals shoot them.

The history of wolves in western Europe is relatively well-known. In the Middle Ages they were common, but the introduction of the poison strychnine and of efficient firearms around the beginning of the 18th century made killing them easy. Their decline began in earnest and continued.

Today wolves survive in only a few places in Europe. According to a recent report by the Council of Europe, they live in about eight of its twenty-three

## THEN & NOW

*The map below shows the former and current distribution of wolves.*

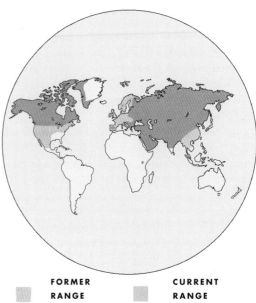

| | |
|---|---|
| **FORMER RANGE** | **CURRENT RANGE** |

**The range of the gray wolf used to cover the entire northern hemisphere, and although at first sight the wolf's present range does not look as though it has diminished by very much on a world scale, the wolf populations within it are sparse and scattered. Loss of temperate forests has been a major cause of decline in numbers. So too has encroachment of its natural habitat by human activities and settlements. However, the greatest losses occur through persecution, and the wolf is only relatively abundant in places too cold for humans to settle.**

*Wolf populations can fluctuate wildly from year to year, and it is only in countries like the United States, where monitoring is constantly being carried out, that the numbers can be reasonably accurate.*

## WOLF POPULATIONS

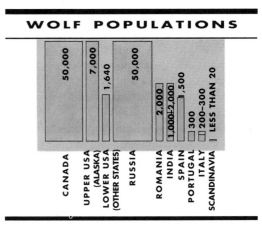

| CANADA | UPPER USA (ALASKA) | LOWER USA (OTHER STATES) | RUSSIA | ROMANIA | INDIA | SPAIN | PORTUGAL | ITALY | SCANDINAVIA |
|---|---|---|---|---|---|---|---|---|---|
| 50,000 | 7,000 | 1,640 | 50,000 | 2,000 | 1,000–2,000 | 1,500 | 300 | 200–300 | LESS THAN 20 |

member states. There is a handful in Scandinavia and some in Italy, Spain, and Portugal.

Wolves start to become more common farther east, in Poland and the former U.S.S.R. There are at least 50,000 wolves in the former U.S.S.R., further emphasizing the fact that the wolf's main haunts today lie in the wild northern lands. There are increasing threats to it even there, however. Timber presents the potential for great profits, and logging companies that have already decimated the forests of the tropics are searching for new and untouched areas.

Despite people's continuing fear of the wolf, there is an increasing recognition that the animal is threatened. Its status across its range is a curious mixture of protection and persecution. In some countries, including the United States, it is strongly protected. In other countries the degree to which protection is enforced leaves something to be desired. In Mongolia, for instance, there are continuing efforts to exterminate it.

In Canada, where the wolf is still relatively abundant, it is fully protected on nature preserves and in national parks, but elsewhere it is still hunted for its pelt. Regulated kills also continue where the wolf is considered to be a threat to livestock or other wild animals.

The history of conservation in North America is the history of predator control. In some places there were bounties on the wolf until relatively recently. One of the main reasons for this was to assure hunters that there would be a high number of the animals they are interested in, especially deer.

Wolf control for the benefit of hunters is by no means a thing of the past. At present there is a planned wolf cull in the Yukon, which is described

## AMAZING FACTS

Many people are terrified of wolves. But despite the fact that they are powerful and potentially dangerous, there have been no known cases of wolves killing people in North America. There have been some attacks. A scientist trying to break up a fight between a wolf and his sled dogs got his arm ripped, and a hunter, doused in deer scent to help him get near his quarry undetected, got pounced on by a wolf.

Why don't wolves attack people? By and large they have not acquired a taste for human flesh; also, humans are too protective of themselves and their young to make it easy for the wolf to stalk humans.

**ENDANGERED SPECIES**

# FROM FORESTS TO FARMLAND

FORMER RANGE OF RED WOLF

In the long-distant past our ancestors lived off the land, roaming through the forests that covered much of the earth, feeding on berries, roots, and any animals they could catch. But as humans evolved abilities such as tool use and communication, it became easier to stay in one place, grow crops, and domesticate animals. Agriculture was born.

Ironically, one of the earliest domesticated animals was the wolf, which gave rise to "man's best friend." Since humans also domesticated some of the wild wolf's prey animals—sheep, wild pigs, and cattle—trouble was bound to follow.

A wolf raiding a sheep fold or a cattle pen could be disastrous for a family, depriving them of their winter meat as well as the means to pay the taxes that kept them in a home. Wolf persecution began.

At first there was plenty of room for both wolves and people. Problems arose mainly when the two were both in the same area, though people also hunted wolves for their warm coats. But as agriculture expanded, the wolves' remaining wild habitats came under increasing pressure.

Today farmland, not forest, covers

S. J. Krasemann/Bruce Coleman Ltd

## CONSERVATION MEASURES

Individual countries with wolf populations must ensure that enough wild areas are set aside for the wolf and that their numbers are carefully monitored. This is already happening in the United States under the auspices of the Endangered Species Act. Accordingly, the federal government has appointed special wolf recovery teams, each team being responsible for its own subspecies.

most of the wolf's original lands. If the wolf is to survive in our agricultural world, it is up to us to make it possible.

Some farmers are turning to organic farming, which is much friendlier to wildlife since the idea is to farm in harmony with nature, not in conflict with it. But on the whole farmers regard wildlife as an enemy, to be obliterated to make room for profitable crops.

The future of wildlife lies with the public and with politicians—and as farming in most parts of the world is heavily subsidized by taxes, if people want farmers to take more care of the land for wildlife they have to demand it—after all, they pay the farmers' bills.

⊃ HELP SCIENTISTS UNDERSTAND THE HABITS ˮ WOLVES SOME ARE TRANQUILIZED AND ʟʟED WITH RADIO COLLARS. THIS ENABLES THE ᴇIENTISTS TO KEEP TRACK OF THE ANIMALS.

ᴎ Europe, the Council of Europe s adopted a manifesto established the IUCN/Wolf Specialist ᴏup. The IUCN is the world's ʀemost conservation body.

Wolves are now increasing in ˡy, Spain, and Portugal.

Restrictions on hunting are ᴡ implemented in several untries.

## WOLVES IN DANGER

THE CHART BELOW SHOWS HOW THE INTERNATIONAL UNION FOR THE CONSERVATION OF NATURE (IUCN), OR THE WORLD CONSERVATION UNION, CLASSIFIES THE STATUS OF THE GRAY WOLF AND SOME OF THE GRAY WOLF SUBSPECIES. THE YEAR IN BRACKETS IS THE DATE OF CLASSIFICATION.

GRAY WOLF      VULNERABLE (1990)

THESE SUBSPECIES ARE THREATENED:
EUROPEAN WOLF
INDIAN WOLF

THESE SUBSPECIES ARE ENDANGERED:
TIBETAN WOLF
ARABIAN WOLF
MEXICAN WOLF

RED WOLF      ENDANGERED (1990)

*ENDANGERED* MEANS THAT THE ANIMAL'S SURVIVAL IS UNLIKELY UNLESS STEPS ARE TAKEN TO SAVE IT. *VULNERABLE* INDICATES THAT THE ANIMAL IS LIKELY TO MOVE INTO THE ENDANGERED CATEGORY FOR SPECIES CONTAINING SUBSPECIES IN DIFFERENT CATEGORIES.

typically as a "caribou recovery program."

On the other hand there are areas where wolf populations have recovered. This is due, at least in part, to the creature's mobility and its tendency to roam; given the opportunity to recolonize an area, the wolf will soon move in.

In Wisconsin, for example, even though the bounty on wolves was lifted in 1957, by the 1960s the animal was thought to be extinct. After the wolf was granted legal protection in the United States in 1974, it gradually recovered in Wisconsin. Animals spread in from neighboring Minnesota, and in the 1980s there were about twenty wolves in four to six packs. In 1990 the population consisted of up to fifty wolves in between six and ten packs.

The wolf is perilously close to the edge of extinction in some countries. In Lebanon, where the animal is offered no protection, there are no more than about ten animals, and these are thought to be just pairs or scattered individuals—"lone wolves." Whether the country's wolves have gained or lost during the years of war remains to be seen.

In Italy, the surviving animals may be threatened

# WOMBATS

Mary Clay/Planet Earth Pictures

# NOSES SHORT AND LONG

ONE CURIOUS LINK BETWEEN THE BUMBLING, BEARLIKE WOMBAT AND THE SCURRYING, SHARP-NOSED BANDICOOTS IS THAT ALL THESE SPECIES HAVE A REAR-OPENING POUCH. SADLY, THEY ARE ALSO BECOMING RARE

There are nearly 270 species of living marsupials (pouched mammals), and about twice as many known fossil species. Today most living species occur in Australia and neighboring New Guinea. They probably originated in what is now North America about 130 million years ago, but marsupial fossils of every shape and size have been found as far apart as Mongolia, Argentina, and Europe. From one branch of this spectacular radiation arose a group of small, flesh-eating marsupials. Some 40 million years ago it split into two groups: One gave rise to the dasyurids—marsupial cats and mice—while the other gave rise to bandicoots and bilbies.

It is likely that, as today, early bandicoots and bilbies lived in forests. This is a poor environment for fossil preservation, so their fossil record is sparse—though a bilbylike fossil five or six million years old has been found in South Australia. Today's bilbies belong to a single family, and the

The wombats, bandicoots, and bilbies are all marsupials, or pouched mammals. Generally, the bandicoots and bilbies are grouped together in the superfamily Perameloidea, while the wombats are in the the superfamily Vombatoidea, which includes the koalas.

**ORDER**
*Marsupialia*

**FAMILY**
*Peramelidae*
(bandicoots)

**GENERA**
*seven*

**SPECIES**
*seventeen*

**FAMILY**
*Thylacomyidae*
(bilbies)

**GENUS**
*Macrotis*

**SPECIES**
*two*

**FAMILY**
*Vombatidae*
(wombats)

**GENERA**
*two*

**SPECIES**
*three*

bandicoots to another. There are nineteen species of bandicoot, ranging in size from that of a mouse to that of a rabbit. Most have coarse brownish or reddish fur with a few stripes over the back. Though the hind legs are longer than the forelegs, they do not show the extreme development of the kangaroos and wallabies. Bandicoots have something of a hunched-up appearance, and can hop, although they often shuffle on all fours.

The long-nosed bandicoot looks a bit like a small kangaroo crossed with a shrew, with grayish brown fur composed of sleek coarse hairs. Unlike a kangaroo it does not hop, but rushes around with short, erratic bursts of speed. This helps it find food and avoid predators. Solitary and nocturnal, it feeds on insects and roots.

### DESERT DWELLERS

The two species of bilby inhabit the central desert regions of Australia, in much drier areas than those inhabited by most bandicoots. Both are rabbit sized and delicately built, with long, soft fur. Strictly nocturnal, bilbies spend the day in a burrow and are active mainly after midnight when the desert is cool, but not too cold. Like bandicoots, they are solitary except when breeding.

Both bilbies and bandicoots have 48 teeth in their long, pointed jaws. They eat insects and share

Jean-Paul Ferrero/Ardea

*Bandicoots* (above) *may be mouse shaped, but many species reach the size of a rabbit.*

## NAME MISTAKES

Many of our names for Australian animals are derived from those originally used by Australian tribal peoples—budgerigar and kangaroo, for example—but not bandicoot. This word comes from "pandi-koku," which in the Indian Hindi language Telegu means "pig-rat" and refers to a large Indian rat that grunts when it feeds. In the early 1800s, British soldiers who had already served in India were sent to southern Australia. Encountering an animal similar to the familiar pandi-koku they gave it their version of the Indian name.

The scientific name for a species usually describes a unique feature—but sometimes it goes wrong. *Choeropus ecaudatus* is the scientific name for the pig-footed bandicoot. *Ecaudatus* means "tailless," but in fact the species has a tail almost as long as its body. Unfortunately, the first specimen to be collected had lost its tail. The scientist, unfamiliar with this animal, took this to be its natural state and named it accordingly.

a similar kind of dentition with other insect-eating mammals, such as moles, shrews, and hedgehogs. In all of these the teeth are small, sharp, and similar in shape and appearance. Between such teeth, insects are quickly sliced into a fine easily digestible pulp. This quickly releases the energy locked up in the food. This is of great help to a small mammal that expends a large proportion of its daily energy needs each day just finding food and staying alive.

In these species, the hind limb is adapted for running or hopping. The fourth toe is large, while the other four are either much reduced or absent. Bandicoots, bilbies, and wombats all have the second and third toes of the hind foot fused together for most of their length, with only the claws being free. In this they differ from all other mammals. These claws make a great comb, and the animals regularly groom themselves with their hind feet. If an animal suffers an accident and loses these toes, it will still try to groom with the stump, never learning to use a forefoot.

### BEARLIKE BURROWER

The big, bearlike wombat is rather more familiar than the little bandicoots or bilbies. But wombats are actually timid and spend much of their time

*The bilby's huge and highly sensitive ears radiate heat and help it keep cool in the desert.*

# THE MARSUPIALS' FAMILY TREE

underground, so surprisingly little has been discovered about their lifestyle. The three wombat species, grouped in two genera, are easily told apart. The common wombat, *Vombatus ursinus* (vom-BAH-tus er-SEEN-us), has coarse fur, a hairless nose, and short, rounded ears. Found in forests, especially on rocky hillsides, it feeds on roots, grass, and fungi and is nocturnal. It digs a burrow with a single entrance, though there may be several emergency refuges in its territory.

Hairy-nosed wombats have finer and softer fur than the common wombat; they have longer, more pointed ears and, as the name suggests, a hairy nose. They are found in dry, open country where they dig complex multientrance burrows and eat mainly grasses. There are two species: the northern, *Lasiorhinus krefftii* (lazz-ee-o-RIE-nus KREF-tee) and the southern, *L. latifrons* (LAT-ee-fronz).

The closest living relative of the wombat is the koala. The koala is essentially a tree-living wombat that split off from the main wombat lineage in the last few million years and became specialized for eating eucalyptus leaves. The big heavy bones of wombats are much more easily fossilized than the small fragile ones of a bandicoot, consequently scientists have a much better idea of wombat history.

### AMIABLE, BUT DIM

Today's wombats are the living descendants of a group that was very successful in the Pleistocene epoch (2 million–10,000 years ago), and included the giant grazing wombats *Diprotodon* (die-PRO-to-don) and *Phascolonus* (fas-coll-O-nuss). *Diprotodon* was the size of a hippo. These marsupials moved in great herds across the grasslands of central Australia. In an adult the massive skull was 20 in (50 cm) long. The jaws were very powerful, but the head was essentially a food-processing structure as the brain of *Diprotodon* was rather small. They are likely to have been amiable, but dim. ∎

*Although from different families, the bandicoots, bilbies, wombats, and koalas represent one branch of the marsupial family tree. Even now, new species are being discovered—particularly among the Australian bandicoots, family Peramelidae (peh-rah-MEL-ee-die)—and it is not always easy to say where one species ends and another begins.*

## HAIRY-NOSED WOMBAT
### *Lasiorhinus*
### (*lazz-ee-o-RIE-nus*)

**As well as the common wombat, there are two species of hairy-nosed wombat: the northern and southern. They differ very little from the common wombat, except in having hair between the nostrils and longer, pointed ears. The southern hairy-nosed wombat is fairly common across its range, but there now remains only a single colony of the northern species, in Queensland. All three wombat species are peaceable burrowers, living on a varied diet of plant matter.**

KOALA

HONEY POSSUM

KANGAROO

CUSCUS & OPOSSUM

Color illustrations Evi Antoniou

B/W illustrations Ruth Grewcock. Koala, cuscus, and honey possum Alan Male/Linden Artists

# EASTERN BARRED BANDICOOT

*Perameles gunnii*
(*peh-RAM-eh-leez GUN-ee-ee*)

The eastern barred bandicoot (right) is one of the Australian long-nosed bandicoots, most of which are distinguished by "tiger stripes" on the lower back. These give excellent camouflage in the grasses covering their arid habitat. Other species of bandicoot prefer moist, tropical rain forests. Active by night, bandicoots eat invertebrates and plant matter.

# BILBY

*Macrotis*
(*mack-RO-tiss*)

There are two species of bilby—the greater and the lesser bilby. They are also known as rabbit-eared bandicoots, for a fairly clear reason. In fact, the long ears are a great asset to these busy little insect-eaters, enabling them to detect the faint rustling of their prey in the arid, sandy grasslands of the Australian interior. The greater bilby is sadly now rare, and the lesser bilby may even be extinct.

MARSUPIAL MOLE

MARSUPIALS

TASMANIAN DEVIL
& OTHER MARSUPIAL CARNIVORES

AMERICAN OPOSSUM

# ANATOMY: THE WOMBAT

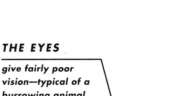

The common wombat (above left) is the largest of the wombats (see Fact File). The giant bandicoot (above right) reaches a head-and-body length of 15–22 in (39–56 cm) with a tail 4.7–13.4 in (12–34 cm) long, while the mouse bandicoot (above center) measures only 6–7 in (15–17.5 cm) from head to rump, with a tail 4.3 in (11 cm) long.

## FEET

The wombat walks on the flats of its feet, rather like humans and bears. The broad feet are armed with long, sturdy claws: five on each forefoot, four on each hind foot. The second and third digits on the foot are partially joined together to make a double-claw, which is used in grooming. When burrowing, the forefeet cut away fresh soil, and the hind feet kick the freshly excavated debris back up the newly dug tunnel.

**HIND FOOT**         **FOREFOOT**

**THE EYES**

give fairly poor vision—typical of a burrowing animal that relies heavily on scent and hearing.

**THE EARS**

are small and rounded, with dense fur on the outer surface. The sense of hearing is good.

**THE NOSE**

is naked with granular skin, like that of a bear or dog. Hairy-nosed wombats have soft, velvety fur between the nostrils. In all species, sense of smell is excellent. The split upper lip enables the wombat to bring its incisors close to the ground to crop low-growing grass.

**THE BODY**

is squat and barrel-like, showing the compact form possessed by many burrowers.

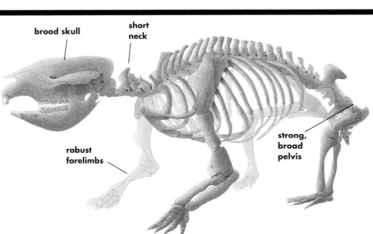

## X-RAY

### SKELETON

The wombat's short, stocky legs and powerful shoulders are built for burrowing. The animal walks on the soles, not the toes of its feet, and cannot run particularly fast, but it compensates by having a greater spread of muscle on the limb bones. Stout bones are a feature of many marsupials, since they help support the weight of a full pouch.

broad skull

short neck

robust forelimbs

strong, broad pelvis

### TEETH

Unlike other marsupials, wombats have rootless, ever-growing incisor teeth (right). This adaptation to gnawing tough grasses is also found in rodents. Another rodentlike feature is the diastema, a large gap between the incisors and the grinding cheek teeth. This space allows large chunks of food to be moved about in the mouth.

X-ray illustrations Elisabeth Smith

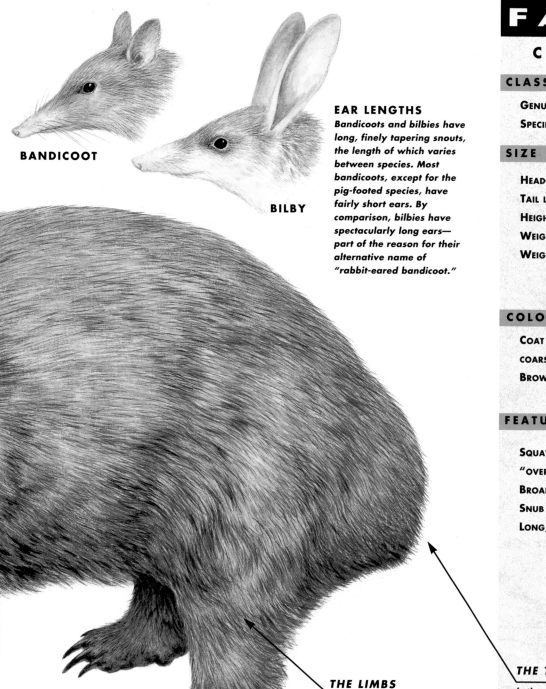

## BANDICOOT

## BILBY

### EAR LENGTHS

*Bandicoots and bilbies have long, finely tapering snouts, the length of which varies between species. Most bandicoots, except for the pig-footed species, have fairly short ears. By comparison, bilbies have spectacularly long ears— part of the reason for their alternative name of "rabbit-eared bandicoot."*

### THE LIMBS

*are not built for running but for burrowing. The short, stout legs enable brief but powerful digging thrusts.*

### THE TAIL

*is tiny and stubby; a long tail would be a hindrance when burrowing.*

---

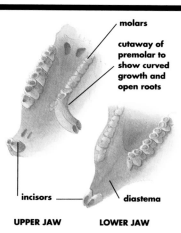

molars

cutaway of premolar to show curved growth and open roots

incisors

**UPPER JAW**

diastema

**LOWER JAW**

### SKULL

*The zygomatic arches of a wombat's skull (near right) flare sideways to make room for enlarged masseter muscles that move the jaws in the side-to-side motion required for grinding tough plant food. Bandicoots (far right) have teeth suited to a diet of both plant and animal matter, with sharp canines and pointed premolars.*

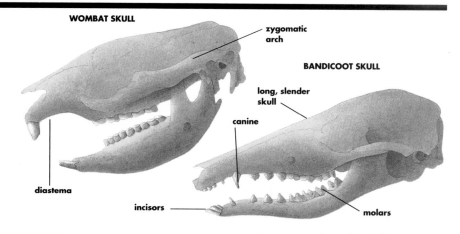

**WOMBAT SKULL**

zygomatic arch

**BANDICOOT SKULL**

long, slender skull

canine

diastema

incisors

molars

# NIGHT FORAGERS

## THE WOMBATS, BANDICOOTS, AND BILBIES HAVE FEW DEFENSES AGAINST ENEMIES. MANY SPECIES ALSO INHABIT VERY ARID CLIMATES, BUT THEY ARE SUPERBLY ADAPTED TO SURVIVE IN THE HOSTILE HEAT

**B**ilbies and wombats are the only two types of marsupial to make a burrow. A bilby digs the tunnel of its burrow in a spiral. This, and its habit of plugging the burrow entrance with sand when it is in residence, helps to confuse visiting predators and to conserve moisture. Bandicoots also enjoy protection, but find a heaped-up pile of vegetation is sufficient. These mounds never have a specific entrance—the bandicoot just snuffles in at any point, heads roughly for the middle, and dozes for most of the day.

### WOMBAT BURROWS

The wombat's burrow system can extend for up to 80 ft (30 m), often with several entrances and with underground connecting tunnels. Shorter burrows from 6–16 feet (2–5 meters) long are dotted about the wombat's territory. These are used for temporary shelter. Each animal may have up to ten burrows in its territory; it visits up to four each night and alternates between three major sleeping burrows. This changing of sleeping quarters may be a device to minimize the buildup of irritating, bloodsucking parasites in the bedding.

The main burrows are usually at the center of the territory. The burrows of hairy-nosed wombats are often excavated at the borders of large clay-pans, where soft limestone is exposed and, for a specialist burrower like the wombat, digging is easier. Common wombats prefer to make their simple burrows along the slopes above creeks and gullies, within tree cover but near open, grassy areas. In these favorable conditions there may be as many as one wombat every five acres (one every two hectares). Within this area, the wombat wanders each night searching for its meals of vegetation; in the process it can travel up to three kilometers (a mile and a half). The home range of a wombat

depends on the amount of food around. It can be as small as 6 acres (2.5 hectares) or as extensive as 57 acres (23 hectares).

### HOME DEFENSE

In the past, wombats must have been the prey of marsupial wolves and marsupial lions, but both these species are now extinct. Dingoes, descended from dogs introduced by the Aborigines, are now the wombats' main enemy. If attacked, a wombat hurries into its burrow, exposing its rump to the

*Bilbies* (above) *are true desert specialists, able to tolerate the extreme heat of Australia's interior.*

Michael Reardon/Tony Stone Worldwide

Kathie Atkinson/Oxford Scientific Films

● When the bilby goes to sleep it does not lie down. Instead, it hunches into a ball by putting its head between its hind legs, then covers its eyes with its ears.

● With their broad, spadelike feet, hairy-nosed wombats can excavate tunnels even in sunbaked ground of concretelike consistency. So great is their muscle power they can make burrows in areas where a man with a pickax has great difficulty even breaking the surface.

● Although the wombat's burrow fits its owner snugly, it is wide enough to allow the wombat to make a U-turn and retrace its steps. It is even claimed that a small child could crawl in; any wombat in residence is more likely to sniff amiably than to bite viciously.

intruder, and may kick backward with both hind feet. The skin is so thick, the tail so short, the fit in the burrow so snug, and the hind feet so powerful and well-clawed that few wombats are killed in a situation such as this. If things get really bad, however, a wombat can show a surprising turn of speed, putting on short sprints at up to 25 mph (40 km/h).

Monitor lizards are the natural enemies of bilbies and bandicoots, as are native hawks. Growing up to 6.5 ft (2 m) in length, monitor lizards can be a threat to both adults and young as their long, sinuous form enables them to penetrate the burrows of bilbies and the nests of bandicoots. Swamp harriers will try for most small marsupials living in moister areas of Australia, while the spotted harrier tries its luck in the more arid areas. Neither bird is particularly big, and they are dangerous mostly to smaller bandicoots and young of the larger species.

In its defense, the long-nosed bandicoot makes a loud alarm call in the form of a shrill squeak. The best that other bandicoots and bilbies manage is a low hiss described as a "huffing," uttered with bared teeth. When set upon, long-nosed bandicoots will gallop rapidly away into the nearest cover. They have been observed jumping straight up into the air and, upon landing, taking off immediately in another direction. ■

*Wombats dislike extreme heat, and take to the surface only when the air has cooled sufficiently.*

# HABITATS

**B**oth bilby species live in Australia. The members of one bandicoot family live—with one exception—in Australia and nearby islands, while the other family, again with one exception, occurs in New Guinea and its nearby islands.

In areas where the climates are similar, Australia and New Guinea may share bandicoot species. So, the rufescent bandicoot occurs in the rain forests of New Guinea and in those on Australia's Cape York Peninsula. Similarly, the brindled bandicoot of northern Australia's grassy woodlands is also found in similar habitats in southern New Guinea. But such overlap is uncommon and, though descended from a common ancestor, the bandicoots of the two landmasses have largely evolved separately over the last 8,000 years. This is partly because the Torres Strait between Australia and New Guinea acts as a barrier to the dispersion of animals and plants, and partly because the climates of the two places differ greatly, with Australia generally being a lot drier than New Guinea.

### LIFE AT DIFFERENT ALTITUDES
In the mountains of New Guinea, species of *Peroryctes* (peh-ro-RIK-teez) bandicoot and of spiny bandicoot (*Echymipera*—eh-kee-mip-EAR-ah)

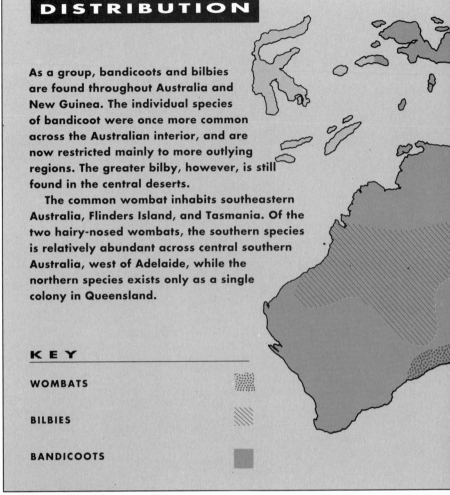

## DISTRIBUTION

As a group, bandicoots and bilbies are found throughout Australia and New Guinea. The individual species of bandicoot were once more common across the Australian interior, and are now restricted mainly to more outlying regions. The greater bilby, however, is still found in the central deserts.

The common wombat inhabits southeastern Australia, Flinders Island, and Tasmania. Of the two hairy-nosed wombats, the southern species is relatively abundant across central southern Australia, west of Adelaide, while the northern species exists only as a single colony in Queensland.

### KEY

WOMBATS

BILBIES

BANDICOOTS

may occur in the same area but be separated by the altitude at which they live. The pale-bellied and giant bandicoots (*Peroryctes*) occur throughout the tropical rain forests of New Guinea—the first from sea level up to 12,800 ft (3,900 m), and the second to 8,860 ft (2,700 m). The long-tailed bandicoot prefers higher altitudes up to 14,764 ft (4,500 m), and the orange-bellied bandicoot occurs in a narrow band from 3,937–4,920 ft (1,200–1,500 m). The reddish spiny bandicoot is common above 3,280 ft (1,000 m), while the brown spiny bandicoot is more common below this. Both live in forests but, while *Peroryctes* bandicoots prefer insects, their spiny cousins are more omnivorous, with a distinct taste for fallen fruit.

Meanwhile, in Australia, long-nosed bandicoots occur at the same altitude but live in areas of different vegetation. The long-nosed bandicoot likes rain forest and dense scrub forest; Bougainville's bandicoot prefers heaths and dunes. The orange bandicoot favors spinifex grassland, while woodland and open country with good ground cover are home to Gunn's bandicoot. Short-nosed bandicoots

*A southern hairy-nosed wombat on the hot, dry Nullarbor Plain in southern Australia.*

Steve Turner/Oxford Scientific Films

are the only bandicoots to occur in both Australia and New Guinea. They prefer open country, with each of the seven species specializing in a different nonforest habitat, from thick swamp grassland to scrublands on dry ridges.

Hairy-nosed wombats occur in semiarid saltbrush and acacia scrub. The areas are characterized by high summer temperatures, low and irregular rainfall, little freestanding water, and frequent droughts. The grasses on which the wombat feeds are very fibrous and have few proteins or nutrients.

### SPECIALIZED SURVIVORS

The semiarid shrublands and tussock grasslands of central Australia are hot, dry environments, with little available water. Bilbies have adapted in several ways. Their large ears radiate excess heat and help them to hear the approach of predators and the scurryings of tiny insect prey. The little fennec fox from the deserts of Africa has similar ears—and it too eats insects. This situation, where two wholly unrelated animals show a similar solution to a similar problem, is known as convergent evolution.

Food can be scarce in the bilbies' arid homeland. But long legs allow them to cover a lot of ground in one night's search for termites, insect larvae, bulbs, fruit, and fungi. In the wild, bilbies do not need to drink, getting all the water they need from the seeds and fruit they occasionally add to their insect diet.

Most bandicoots live in insect-rich forests and so do not have to go far to find food. Consequently, their legs are shorter and, since they find their food by rummaging around in leaf litter, their eyes are smaller to avoid damage from twigs and thorns. The long legs also help keep the body off hot sand in the day and away from the cold ground at night.

### DESERT WOMBATS

Hairy-nosed wombats have adapted to their harsh, semiarid scrub environment by evolving a lifestyle that minimizes the expenditure of energy. This includes a very low rate of metabolism—about two-thirds that expected for a marsupial of its size—a relatively variable body temperature, and a low requirement for nitrogen. Furthermore, there is a very long interval between the ingestion of food and its excretion as feces. This extended time enables the wombat to extract every scrap of goodness out of the food in its guts.

These desert wombats also produce highly concentrated urine and almost bone-dry feces, helping to minimize the loss of vital body fluids. The camel has long been thought of as the ultimate desert survivalist; but while a water-deprived camel loses 2.7 oz (76 g) of water for every 3.5 oz (100 g) of feces it excretes, the hairy-nosed wombat in a comparable

*Bandicoots have evolved to become "all-rounders," able to colonize habitats from forests to arid scrub.*

Pat Morris/Ardea

situation loses only 1.3 oz (38 g) of water. In addition, being nocturnal minimizes water loss through respiration (panting), and, as the burrow systems are constructed to maintain maximum humidity, this too helps the wombat cut down on water loss.

The teeth of wombats also help in this regard. Both the incisors and the molars are ever-growing and wear away in such a way as to maintain

## TEMPERATURE AND RAINFALL

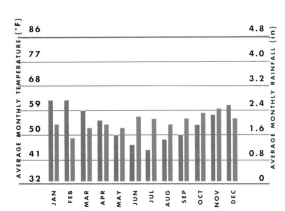

- **TEMPERATURE**
- **RAINFALL**

*In its exposed location between two mainlands, Flinders is at times a hostile place, with temperatures falling below freezing point in winter. It enjoys a mild summer, while escaping the fierce heat of Australia's desert interior.*

extremely sharp shearing faces on the opposing sides of the upper and lower teeth. This erosion forms an extremely efficient dental mill that finely slices the highly fibrous diet of grasses. In chewing grasses, the wombat is even more efficient than its grazing neighbor the kangaroo. While the kangaroo grinds most of its food into millimeter-sized morsels, more than half of the wombat's feed ends up in bits less than half a millimeter in diameter. This grassy mush attains the same consistency as that chewed up by rodents only a hundredth of the wombat's size. For the wombat, this means it can eat coarser grasses, extract more nutrients out of them, and use less water when excreting them. The parallels with rodents extend further; there is some evidence that wombats are evolving cheek pouches—a feature that rodents already have and that many of them use as a sort of fleshy sack for storing food.

Common wombats share the adaptations of their arid-land cousins, though in a less extreme form. In temperatures above 79°F (26°C) a wombat can suffer from heatstroke, so in the heat of a summer's day it remains six feet (almost two meters) underground, in the cool of its burrow. In winter, however, the daytime air temperature in the burrow is around 39°F (4°C); this is too cool for a wombat's comfort, so then it spends a lot of the day outside, either basking in the sun or looking around for food. ■

Dave Watts/ANT/NHPA

## FLINDERS ISLAND

**Flinders Island is a small, uninhabited rock block off the northwest coast of Tasmania. Little disturbed, it has much of its original flora, including eucalyptus forests and grasslands. The island hosts a number of rare species native to Australia, including bandicoots, wallabies, and some rare Australian mice. Also present is the southern hairy-nosed wombat, which is threatened on the mainland by agriculture and diseases.**

**Introductions onto islands, which can provide rare species with safe havens, play a big part in Australia's conservation drive. Wombats were first transferred to Flinders in the 1960s, and there are now some 200 individuals on the island. Conservationists hope to draw from the island stock to reintroduce wombats to some of their former habitats. They also hope to apply the techniques learned from this introduction to programs involving the much rarer northern hairy-nosed wombat.**

### NEIGHBORS

**The waters around Flinders are frequently stormy, but they are rich in marine life. The island itself, replete with grassland and forests, is a haven for several endemic Tasmanian species.**

**SHORT-BEAKED ECHIDNA**

*One of only three mammals to lay eggs, the echidna catches ants with a long, sticky tongue.*

**TASMANIAN PADEMELON**

*These small, nocturnal kangaroos travel through dense undergrowth along tunnel-like runways.*

Neighbor illustrations Richard Tibbitts

VICTORIA

Bass
Strait

Flinders
Island

TASMANIA

**EASTERN QUOLL**

This cat-sized marsupial carnivore has suffered from introduced competitors and their diseases.

**AUSTRALIAN FUR SEAL**

A subspecies of the Cape fur seal, this mammal is a common sight in the Bass Strait north of Tasmania.

**HUMPBACK WHALE**

The humpback is one of the rorqual group of whales, distinguished by their grooved throats.

**SHEERWATER**

Breeding in cliff-top burrows, this master aerial acrobat takes fish from the sea's surface.

**BELL MYNAH**

Nesting in large colonies in forested gullies, this honeyeater is named after its pleasant "tink" call.

# FOOD AND FEEDING

Feeding at night, the long-nosed bandicoot inserts its long, sensitive snout into crevices to probe for prey. It also digs in the soil with its strong fore claws. When it finds a victim, it first rakes it rapidly with the forefeet to kill it. Invertebrate prey includes flies and their larvae, earthworms, earwigs, spiders, adult and larval beetles, moths, ants, and termites. In fact, the bandicoot seems to eat whatever crawling thing it comes across.

Since the bandicoot finds most of its prey in the topsoil, the ground in its home range is often pockmarked with shallow holes. As bandicoots sometimes live in towns, this can lead to conflict with gardeners who do not appreciate the telltale craters in their lawns. However, bandicoots are on the whole beneficial because of the great quantities of crop-destroying insects that they eat. Some plant food is eaten, but it is consumed quite selectively. Reflecting the lack of dental and digestive adaptations for dealing with fibrous plant materials, bandicoots eat mostly soft fruits in season.

The brindled bandicoot moves slowly over the whole of its 2.5–12-acre (1–5-hectare) range, spending little time in any one place. This characteristic foraging pattern is an adaptation to finding small, scattered food items. An alternative strategy is used by short-nosed bandicoots, which will spend several days in one small area, scratching up the surface in a search for insects and worms, before moving to another part of the territory. They will only eat living, moving prey.

Living in drier, tougher conditions, bilbies cannot afford to be choosy and will eat almost any small animal, including insects, snails, and small vertebrates such as mice, frogs, and fledgling birds. They also eat grass seeds and sedge roots.

## A CAPABLE DIGESTION

A bandicoot's digestive system needs to cope with a wide variety of food forms, so it has become generalized, with a simple stomach and small intestine. There is, however, a well-developed cecum to hold plant-digesting bacteria. The intestine also has special enzymes to break down trehalose, a sugar found only in insects. Food takes around nine hours to pass through the bandicoot's gut; this is slightly longer than in purely carnivorous marsupials, since plant food is less easily digested than animal food.

## GRAZERS AND BROWSERS

Each individual wombat has a personal feeding area, within which it uses regular paths to favored sites. Once there, it uses its forefeet or jaws to grasp and tear the vegetation. Hairy-nosed wombats crop grasses, while the common wombat browses for roots, tree bark, leaves, shrubs, and fungi.

## EAT ANYTHING

*Food can be hard to come by in the bilbies' arid habitat. They will eat almost any animal they can overpower, as well as seeds and other plant parts* (right).

Illustrations Simon Turvey/Wildlife Art Agency

*The long bandicoot snout is used
to expose hidden prey* (above).

### INSECT-KILLERS

*Bandicoots* (above)
*feed mainly on various
invertebrates. Some
species will devour
mice, having first
beaten them to a pulp
with their forelimbs.*

### GENTLE GRAZERS

*Wombats* (left) *are
purely vegetarian in
their diet. Depending
on the species, they feed
on grasses, shrubs,
roots, leaves, or bark.*

Wombats have some peculiar digestive adaptations. The stomach has glands that are thought to
help digest fibrous plant matter, but, unusually,
most of the digestion occurs not in the stomach but
in the colon. This huge colon comprises over two-
thirds of the volume of the intestine and houses
vast concentrations of bacteria. Through a process
called microbial fermentation, the bacteria break
down the vegetation mashed into little particles by
the wombat's fine-chopping teeth. The smaller the
particles of food, the more easily and rapidly the
bacteria can act upon them.

Nevertheless, a meal is generally retained in the
wombat's gut for a very long time: 95–210 hours.
This gives the bacteria every chance to wring out all
the goodness from the particles, which the wombat
then takes up through the lining of its intestine,
while leaving enough for the bacteria to survive. ■

## in SIGHT

### FUNGUS-FRIENDLY

**Bilbies and Australian bandicoots eat fungi
during the brief part of the year that the
spore-producing bodies (mushrooms) are
aboveground. The spores pass through the
body and emerge unharmed in the feces. In
dispersing the fungi, bandicoots and
bilbies are benefiting the entire ecosystem.
This is because fungi break down dead
material, which in turn restores nutrients to
growing tree and shrub roots.**

**The marsupials play an important role
after a bushfire, when heat has killed off
many of the fungi. Then the scrabbling
actions of their feeding forays often
unearth living roots, which the spores in
their feces can grow into and colonize.**

# TERRITORY

Adult male bilbies have a number of exclusive burrows that they scent mark with their anal glands. They may share these with one or more females and their young. The males in an area have a rigid dominance hierarchy, but this is established without fighting.

Males of most bandicoot species have been reported to act extremely aggressively when meeting with others. In captivity, bandicoots have been observed to ignore one another if the enclosure is big enough. But in a tighter space, they fight with open mouths, viciously scrabbling at each other with the long claws on their forefeet. Indeed, a female only accepts the presence of a male when she is sexually receptive. This intolerance is common in animals where food is patchily distributed; the vital energy resources of life are spread too unpredictably to permit the animals to share them.

---

**HAIRY-NOSED WOMBAT WARRENS FEATURE A NUMBER OF ENTRANCES LINKED BELOW GROUND BY TUNNELS**

---

The territory of most male bandicoots is two to three times larger than that of a female. The male's territory will encompass those of several females, and he will try and mate with each if he can, while defending "his" females from other male intruders. This involves a rapid nightly tour of his territory, which serves to detect rogue males and find out which females are ready to mate. In species from moister areas this can become an almost full-time job, as a female is capable of bearing up to five litters a year. Species in more arid areas stop breeding in the dry season.

### PEACEABLE WOMBATS

The wombat's social behavior is adapted to saving energy. And since fighting can be exhausting, wombat territories are laid out with a view to minimizing conflict. Though they may visit each other's burrows, only a single wombat occupies each burrow. Territories become important in the breeding season, however, when male aggression rises.

Centered on the burrow, territories are marked with dung, and the boundaries are clearly recognized by all neighboring wombats. Encounters are few, and when they do occur they are likely to be amiable. Rare fights involve attempts to bite each other on the ear or flank. Hairy-nosed wombats may actually cluster their burrows to form a warren; this may be

*In the cool of the evening, a common wombat nudges her young out from the safety of the burrow.*

650–980 ft (200–300 m) across and house five to ten wombats. Males generally stay in the central warren, and females move between warrens. But these warrens can be deceptive: Hairy-nosed wombats are basically solitary, each individual possessing its own burrow and feeding area.

Interactions between a mother and her young, however, are characteristically amiable, and young wombats learn to burrow by digging small subsystems off their mother's burrows. However, some four months after leaving their mother's pouch they leave to set up house on their own.

As with all animal territories, the size of the defended area is related to the amount of food within it, so territories in food-rich areas will tend to be smaller than those in areas where resources are few and far between. But this flexibility does not depend solely upon a territory's geographical location—it is also linked to the changing seasons. At barren times of the year, individuals may range far and wide in search of a meal. Such wanderings can lead to much more frequent contacts between normally solitary individuals. For a wombat, keeping to the rules of energy conservation is vitally important at this critical time, since food sources are at a premium. As a result, having already used up precious calories with long-distance foraging, and unable to foot the energy bill involved in fighting—or afford the extra cost invoked by tissue repair—wombats actually become less aggressive at times of low food availability.

### NEW GUINEA CANNIBALS

Little is known about the territoriality of New Guinea bandicoots—due mainly to the difficulties of studying animals of the deep rain forest. However, captive studies indicate that, like many insect-eaters, New Guinea bandicoots are highly aggressive toward each other and will sometimes fight to the death. On such occasions the victor gets a nutrient supplement—in the form of the supine body of the loser.

The few existing studies in the wild have shown that a New Guinea bandicoot often wanders around its territory on a fairly random basis, searching for insects. This makes it difficult for it to mark specific spots regularly as territorial boundaries. Because of this, scent glands on the body are almost constantly active, infusing the territory with its own particular odor as it snuffles through the undergrowth of the Papuan rain forest. ■

ANT/NHPA

**SUN SPOTS**
*Shallow scrapes, dug above the wombat's burrows, are used for early-morning sunbathing.*

### in SIGHT

### ENERGY EFFICIENT

Outside the breeding season, wombats are typically passive, congenial creatures. This peaceable nature and lethargic lifestyle actually relates to the wombat's diet; tough grasses do not provide high-protein, quick-release energy. So the wombat digests slowly and takes life easy.

The use of long-passage digestion—to extract the full nutrient and energy value from unfavorable food—is not unique to the wombat. It is also used by such animals as howler monkeys and sloths. Like the wombat, they all feed on vegetation that is very poor in available nutrients.

Another feature that these animals have in common is dense, shaggy fur. Even though they live in the tropics, the food gives them so little fuel that they have little energy to spare for actively keeping warm—hence the thick and furry insulation.

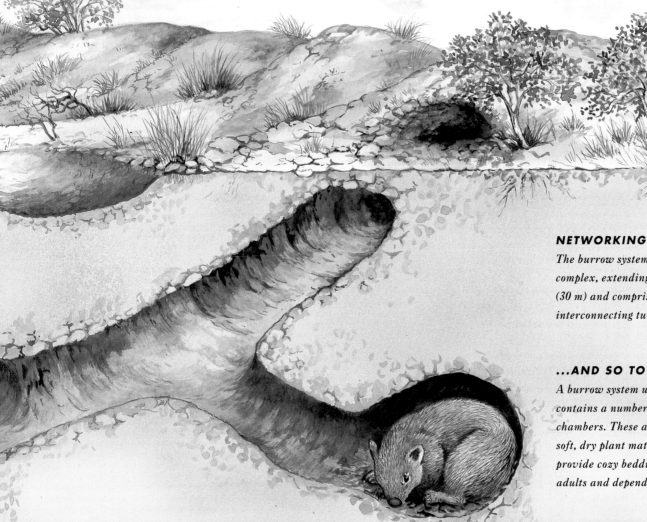

### NETWORKING

*The burrow system is often complex, extending up to 98 ft (30 m) and comprising several interconnecting tunnels.*

### ...AND SO TO BED

*A burrow system usually contains a number of nesting chambers. These are lined with soft, dry plant material to provide cozy bedding for both adults and dependent young.*

# LIFE CYCLE

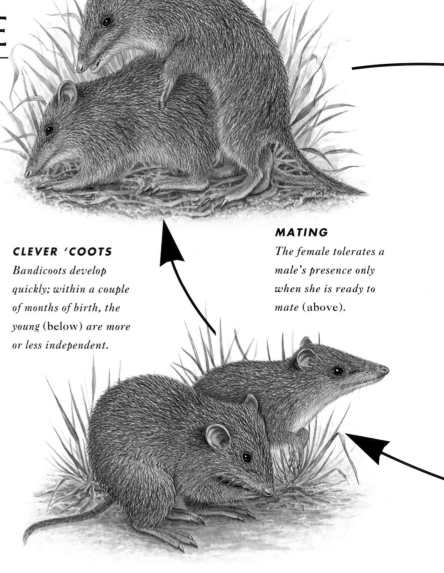

**M**arsupial reproduction depends heavily on the weather. In wet areas—such as tropical rain forests—females can breed all year-round; in drier areas they time births to coincide with maximum food abundance. Bilbies, for example, breed mainly from March to May (the southern autumn), when rainfall is highest.

In dense vegetation, expectant long-nosed bandicoots construct a mound of twigs, leaves, and earth and give birth in a hole in its center. In more open areas, however, they will excavate a nest chamber, line it with plant fibers, and then cover this with a twiggy mound. In areas where mound making is difficult, bandicoots nest in abandoned rabbit burrows, rock piles, and hollow logs.

---

BANDICOOTS AND BILBIES HAVE
THE SHORTEST REPRODUCTION CYCLES
OF ANY MAMMAL SPECIES

---

Having mated in her burrow, a female bilby gives birth to one to three young after a pregnancy of some twenty-one days. She possesses eight teats in a rear-opening pouch. The newborn young attach their mouths firmly to the teats and do not vacate the pouch until seventy to seventy-five days later. Some fourteen days after that, they are weaned. During this time, they will still try and leap into the pouch if danger threatens. A female long-nosed bandicoot will not be receptive again for about two months after giving birth, though this still means that she can produce three to four litters in a season.

**CLEVER 'COOTS**
*Bandicoots develop quickly; within a couple of months of birth, the young* (below) *are more or less independent.*

**MATING**
*The female tolerates a male's presence only when she is ready to mate* (above).

## POUCH VARIATIONS

**In most marsupials the pouch opens forward. Female wombats, however, are one of the few marsupials that have the opening to the pouch facing backward. This shields the baby while the mother is moving underground and prevents earth from entering the furry nursery and possibly smothering the infant. An even more extreme development is found in the South American yapok. This stream-loving opossum has a ring of sphincter muscles around the mouth of the pouch, which close it off like a duffel bag every time the yapok enters the water—so preventing the enclosed babies from drowning.**

B/W illustrations Ruth Grewcock

Color illustrations Wayne Ford/Wildlife Art Agency

# GROWING UP

*The life of a young golden bandicoot*

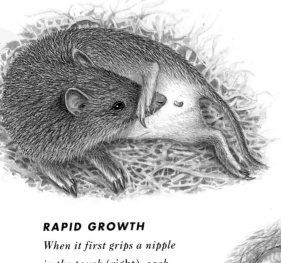

### WALK OF LIFE

*A newborn bandicoot crawls from the birth canal to the pouch (left). In many species, newborns are born with special claws for this purpose; these are later shed.*

### RAPID GROWTH

*When it first grips a nipple in the pouch (right), each newborn is smaller than a bean. By the time the young are ready to emerge, the female is having trouble walking (below).*

## FROM BIRTH TO DEATH

| COMMON WOMBAT | LONG-NOSED BANDICOOT |
|---|---|
| **MATING:** ANYTIME | |
| **GESTATION:** 20–22 WEEKS | **GESTATION:** 12–13 DAYS |
| **NO. OF YOUNG:** 1, RARELY 2 | **NO. OF YOUNG:** 1–5 |
| **WEIGHT AT BIRTH:** 0.07 oz (2 G) | **WEIGHT AT BIRTH:** NOT KNOWN |
| **TIME IN POUCH:** 6–7 MONTHS | **TIME IN POUCH:** 48–53 DAYS |
| **WEANING:** 8–9 MONTHS | **WEANING:** 59–61 DAYS |
| **SEXUAL MATURITY:** 23 MONTHS | **SEXUAL MATURITY:** 3 MONTHS IN FEMALE, 4 MONTHS IN MALE |
| **LONGEVITY:** 6–10 YEARS IN THE WILD, UP TO 27 YEARS RECORDED IN CAPTIVITY | **LONGEVITY:** 3 YEARS OR MORE IN CAPTIVITY; UNKNOWN IN WILD |

Bandicoots have eight nipples, but usually raise three or four young at a time. This is because each new litter is generally born just as the previous one is weaned. Nipples used by the previous litter swell up as the babies develop, and would be too large for the newborns, but because there are four spare nipples, the new young are assured a source of milk. Meanwhile, the nipples unused in this reproductive session slowly diminish in size, getting ready to feed the next batch of babies.

Hairy-nosed wombats give birth in the spring (October–January), if there has been sufficient rain. Common wombats have no such complications: Their young can be born at any time of year.

A female wombat usually gives birth to a single young weighing 0.07 oz (2 g) and measuring 0.9 in (22 mm). The baby stays in the pouch for six or seven months. Weaned at eight or nine months, it leaves the mother soon afterward. It becomes sexually mature at twenty-three months in common wombats, and at eighteen months in hairy-nosed wombats. ■

*Two young northern brown bandicoots head for the warmth and safety of their mother's pouch (below).*

## in SIGHT

### BABY FACTORY

The golden bandicoot has the briefest gestation of any mammal: just twelve days. The tiny newborns enter the pouch and suckle for seven weeks; the pouch expands as they grow until it almost brushes the ground. Ten days after the young emerge, they are weaned and on their own as their mother ceases to care for them. Within three months the new females can start families of their own. This rapid cycle allows the golden bandicoot to exploit new sources of food and to respond quickly when bushfires decimate the population.

ANT/NHPA

# DRIVEN FROM COVER

## MOST MARSUPIALS ARE IN TROUBLE AND THE WOMBATS, BANDICOOTS, AND BILBIES ARE NO EXCEPTION. THANKFULLY, THE AUSTRALIAN GOVERNMENT IS NOW MAKING EVERY EFFORT TO SAVE THEM

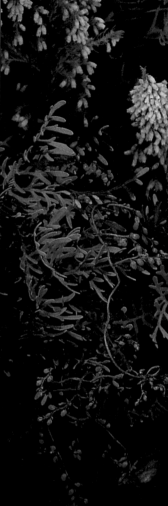

**B**andicoots and bilbies have suffered one of the greatest declines of all marsupial groups. Today, almost all species are threatened in some way, with those of the arid and semiarid zones being particularly affected. The pig-footed bandicoot and lesser bilby have not been seen in over fifty years and are probably extinct. Others, like the greater bilby, have lost many of their subspecies. Some species are at risk because of naturally low numbers or restricted ranges. Examples of these include the Seram Island long-nosed mouse bandicoot; this species was discovered in 1900 and has never been seen again. Only four specimens are known—all from moss-covered forests high on one mountain on Seram, southwest of New Guinea. The tiny New Guinea mouse bandicoot lives in similar habitats in New Guinea. Though it is rarely seen, its small size means it is easily overlooked and scientists hope it is more common than it appears to be.

### THREATS TO SURVIVAL

However, for most species there is little room for optimism. A major problem is that of introduced predators, such as the cat, fox, and rat, which eat adults and babies. Rabbits, too, have disturbed the native species. The solitary bandicoots and bilbies are no match for a warren of rabbits, that eat both the marsupials' food plants and those which give shade and shelter. The small marsupials' traditional enemy, the native species of hawk, falcon, and snake, have learned that rabbits make a good meal. As rabbit numbers have increased, so have those of the predators, which simply makes things worse for the bilbies and bandicoots.

Many bandicoots and bilbies were once hunted for their valuable pelts. Hunting in Australia was particularly intense between 1850 and 1930; in fifty years, over 21 million marsupials were killed in the state of New South Wales alone. Some were shot as vermin, others had more bizarre uses: In Tasmania, wombats were once killed for their bristly pelts, which were fashioned into doormats. Combined with the problems from introduced predators and competitors, hunting drove many populations down to critically low levels.

The rabbit-eared bilby was once widespread over much of the dry interior of Australia. It now occurs in scattered populations in the Tanami, Great Sandy, and Gibson Deserts, some 20 percent of its former range. Although it was abundant at the time of the early white settlers, concerns for its future survival were being expressed as early as the 1850s. Factors in its decline include changed scrub-burning regimes from those used by Aboriginals, predation by foxes, and alteration of habitat by

John Downer/Oxford Scientific Films

*The fox* (above), *introduced to Australia by settlers, has killed countless native marsupials.*

Dave Watts/ANT/NHPA

*This map shows the former and present
distribution of the golden bandicoot.*

FORMER
DISTRIBUTION

PRESENT
DISTRIBUTION

**The range of the golden bandicoot has
declined greatly in the 200 years since the
European settlement of Australia. The home
of this species once extended deep into the
interior. Human expansion, agriculture,
introduced predators, and food competitors
caused the death of so many individuals
that this animal is now confined to the
northwest Kimberleys in Western
Australia—in particular the coastal Prince
Regent Flora and Fauna Reserve—and a
few islands off the adjacent coast.**

rabbits. The foxes and rabbits followed crews laying
the first telegraphs across Australia, and so reached
remote areas even before the main waves of white
settlers. Rabbits also ate foods especially favored by
young bilbies, preventing juvenile recruitment to the
population so that gradually it withered away.
Today, bilby colonies often comprise a handful of
individuals and are usually widely scattered. One
recent survey found only six small colonies in
almost 1,544 sq miles (4,000 sq km) of woodland in
the MacDonald Ranges north of Alice Springs.

Even the golden bandicoot's phenomenal reproductive powers have not helped it, and it is now
almost extinct on the Australian mainland. One of

*Livestock now occupy much of its habitat, but the
southern brown bandicoot has not yet become rare.*

# OUT OF ACTION

## DISEASES

Bilbies and bandicoots did not suffer when the myxomatosis virus was released in Australia to control rabbits; the fleas that carried the disease preferred rabbit blood.

Wombats have been less lucky. They are sensitive to sarcoptic mange, a skin disease caused by a mite. Though wombats have their own skin mites, those from introduced dogs and cats seem to favor wombats, too. The resulting infections can wipe out whole wombat colonies. Wombats can also catch the foot-and-mouth virus from cattle and, like all marsupials, they are also highly susceptible to tuberculosis.

Like any animal, marsupials have a range of naturally occurring diseases to which they are usually resistant. But these can become fatal if the animals are forced into marginal habitats or become stressed through hunting, pollution, or overcrowding.

the great problems for this species was the introduction of cattle, which grazed away the plants in which it rooted for insect food. This problem has also affected the rabbit-eared bilby.

### PERSECUTED WOMBATS

Both species of hairy-nosed wombats declined with the spread of European settlers across Australia. They were persecuted because their burrows were thought to be dangerous to livestock and to horses, which might easily break a leg in one of the burrow system's many entrances.

Introduced rabbits competed with the wombats for the sparse grasses of their arid region home. On top of this, the farmers shot the wombats in an attempt to eradicate the rabbits, which often used the wombat burrows as shelter. Living in dry areas susceptible to drought and famine, such persecution worsened the naturally tough situation faced by these animals. The northern hairy-nosed wombat now occurs only in one small locality. The southern species is doing a little better, but its populations are small, fragmented, and isolated.

### RISKS OF INBREEDING

Under normal conditions, natural influx or emigration, plus large population sizes, ensures that there is a high degree of genetic variation in most populations. But if the population is small and isolated,

ENDANGERED SPECIES

Steve Turner/Oxford Scientific Films

# THE NORTHERN HAIRY-NOSED WOMBAT

WOMBATS IN QUEENSLAND

As a large, ground-living grazer with an already tough life in the arid grasslands of Australia, the hairy-nosed wombat was ill-equipped to deal with any further pressures. Consequently, hunting, the introduction of alien mammals, such as rabbits, goats, sheep, and camels, and drastic changes in the way the grasslands were burned have caused an unprecedented slump in populations and the distributional range of the hairy-nosed wombat. Not only have the alien grazing animals taken over its food sources, but they have also brought with them diseases to which the wombat has little natural resistance.

Before its troubles started, the northern hairy-nosed wombat could have been found over most of east-central Australia, and its honeycomb burrows lunar-landscaped the ground on many a scrubby slope. But its energy-conscious lifestyle could not adjust to disturbance and this marsupial's decline has been swift.

Today, only one population of the northern hairy-nosed species remains. Found in east-central Queensland, it consists of some 60–70 burrows spread over an area of about 5.8 sq miles (15 sq km), inside Epping

## CONSERVATION MEASURES

● Trade is prohibited in Bougainville's bandicoot, the greater and lesser bilby, and the hairy-nosed wombat. In addition, these wombats are fully protected in Australia and the common wombat also has some degree of protection in some states.

● The year 1992 saw the development of the "Australian National Strategy for the Conservation of Species and Communities

Forest National Park. Conservationists are unwilling to disturb the colony and have not made a census, but they guess that it contains no more than about 65 individuals.

Ten species of marsupials are known to have gone extinct in recent times, and the Queensland National Parks and Wildlife Service is making all efforts to ensure that the hairy-nosed wombat does not become number eleven.

They have drawn up a comprehensive Species Recovery Plan, which includes such conservation measures as fencing out cattle, monitoring fires, and keeping away dingoes. In other parts of Epping Park, rangers are assisting with the regeneration of the types of vegetation that the wombat likes, in the hope of providing a new home for any individuals that may strike out on their own and found a new colony.

Inset ANT/NHPA

## WOMBATS AND BANDICOOTS IN DANGER

ALL SPECIES ARE DECLINING TO A GREATER OR LESSER DEGREE AND ARE GIVEN PROTECTION ACROSS MOST OF THEIR RANGE. FURTHERMORE, THE FOLLOWING ARE LISTED BY THE INTERNATIONAL UNION FOR THE CONSERVATION OF NATURE (IUCN) IN ITS *RED DATA BOOK*:

| | |
|---|---|
| GOLDEN BANDICOOT | ENDANGERED |
| WESTERN BARRED BANDICOOT | ENDANGERED |
| EASTERN BARRED BANDICOOT | VULNERABLE |
| CLARA BANDICOOT | RARE |
| FLY RIVER BANDICOOT | INSUFFICIENTLY KNOWN |
| GIANT BANDICOOT | EXTINCT |
| SERAM BANDICOOT | INDETERMINATE |
| | |
| GREATER BILBY | VULNERABLE |
| | |
| NORTHERN HAIRY-NOSED WOMBAT | ENDANGERED |

RARER THAN EVER: THE NORTHERN HAIRY-NOSED WOMBAT CANNOT SURVIVE WITHOUT PROTECTION.

Threatened with Extinction" and the passage of the Endangered Species Protection Act. The act identifies which species are vulnerable or endangered and promotes recovery plans. Listed are 1,025 species, including 44 mammals.

● Also published in 1992 was the Action Plan for the Conservation of Australian Marsupials and Monotremes (echidnas and the platypus).

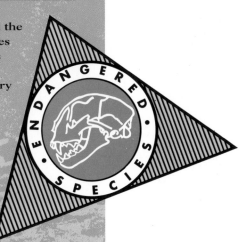

there may be only a few breeding partners. Over the generations, the members of a population become more closely related, and the amount of genetic variation among individuals is reduced. Under such circumstances, inbreeding increases and viability and fertility are often reduced, especially if the population remains under threat and cannot quickly grow to fill its original range. This cycle of problems, begetting more problems, is often referred to as the "extinction vortex."

In the long term, populations with a reduced genetic variability are less able to respond to new environmental pressures, such as a change in climate or a new evolutionary development by a food item. Conservation biologists, aware of such potentialities, monitor the health and levels of genetic diversity of small populations. Where practical, animals may be swapped between populations to help maintain genetic diversity.

### STRESSED BANDICOOTS

Quite naturally, populations may undergo short-term oscillations in their numbers. Normally this would be solved by animals migrating away from overcrowded areas and founding new colonies elsewhere. However, where only tiny patches of suitable habitats are left this is no longer possible. Under such conditions, densities can build up to such an extent that many animals simply die of stress. The survivors, weakened by persistent high-density bickering, may fail to breed with the rapidity needed to ensure a recovery, and the population may die out. This effect has been observed

# ALONGSIDE MAN

## TAILS OF WOE

**Australian Aboriginals have always hunted bandicoots and bilbies. In addition to hunting them for their meat, they use bundles of the black-and-white tails of bilbies as personal adornments. Aboriginals catch a bandicoot by jumping on its nest, holding the animal down, and killing it. Bilbies are caught by digging out their burrows.**

**In the more remote areas of New Guinea, bandicoots are still an important item of food. Such hunting need not endanger local populations if conducted on a sustainable basis. Conservationists are advocates of ensuring the local people's hunting rights, since there is often a cultural reverence for the region's forests—the traditional source of livelihood.**

in the mouse bandicoot, *Isoodon obsoletus*, which, fortunately, is still common enough for such events not to endanger the species' overall survival. It does, however, bode badly for other small, rare species such as the related golden bandicoot.

### SITTING DUCKS

Today many conservation plans focus on keeping introduced predators out of the protected area. This is not surprising, in view of the disastrous effect these exotics have had on Australia's native wildlife. Few of the modern marsupials evolved to eat other marsupials—with a few exceptions, such as the marsupial cats and the now probably extinct marsupial wolf. If they are not herbivores, marsupials generally eat insects, carrion, or smaller vertebrates such as frogs. Australia's marsupials were easy prey for introduced carnivores, and the 200 years since European settlement has simply not been long enough to enable native mammals to evolve effective defenses. Consequently, wherever they find marsupials, introduced mammalian predators find easy prey.

The fox, originally brought to Australia to provide a pastime for homesick European huntsmen, has long been one of the prime killers of Australian marsupials. It is notably absent from those areas where native mammals have declined least—for example, Tasmania, northern Australia, eastern Australia's moist forests, and many islands. Recent fox control programs have boosted the survival rates for rare native species. Australian biologists now know that feral cats, too, are major predators on native animals. Not only have cats killed off many island species, they have even compounded the failure of conservation programs, devouring bilbies and golden bandicoots that had been returned

*Wombats have charm aplenty. They have been kept as affectionate, if occasionally grumpy, family pets.*

to areas in recolonization attempts. The biologists learned the hard way that such attempts only work if you first wipe out the predator that caused the demise in the first place.

### NEW GUINEA SPECIES

The situation has been less fraught on the island of New Guinea. Foxes have not been successfully introduced there, and, though cats have come in as pets, they have largely failed to colonize rural areas, perhaps because New Guinea's moister, more forested habitat does not suit them so well as the drier areas of Australia, and also because human populations are sparser. Dogs, an occasional pest in Australia, occur in New Guinea, but most are found in rural villages where they are kept for hunting. Packs of true feral dogs are said to be uncommon—much to the benefit of the wildlife.

It is thought that several kinds of deep-forest bandicoots are threatened by the development of roads and dams and by the effects of logging. One of the spiny bandicoots has a highly restricted range, and is believed to be endangered mostly from the hunting activities of tribal New Guineans, who consider its flesh a delicacy. ∎

Patrick Fagot/HNPA

# INTO THE FUTURE

Of all mammal species to have become extinct worldwide in the past 200 years, 50 percent have come from Australia. Out of a mammal fauna of 245, 16 are believed to be extinct and 26 now occur only as small populations occupying less than 20 percent of their former range. In the light of this tragic situation, Australian conservation efforts are being supported by government initiatives that include wildlife laws, species recovery programs, and a specially targeted system of protected areas.

But it is not enough to declare an area protected. It is often necessary to eradicate introduced pest species and to re-create habitats that were previously destroyed. In some cases, threatened populations must be moved wholesale to better areas where their chances of survival are improved.

The eastern barred bandicoot is now restricted to one colony around the city of Hamilton. The

## PREDICTION

### GONE BEFORE THEIR TIME?

*Bilbies and hairy-nosed wombats, the focus of a great deal of work, are likely to survive. But for some species the problems are overwhelming and help has come too late. New species of marsupial continue to be discovered, especially in New Guinea. Sadly, some of these will die out without our even having known of their existence.*

most recent census put the population at 633 animals. This population is protected, but is critically small and could become weakened by inbreeding. Studies are under way to see how young animals disperse from the maternal nest. If they disperse effectively, gene flow is improved enough to reduce the likelihood of inbreeding.

Elsewhere, studies on the territorial short-nosed bandicoot are looking at how the stress of living at high densities may affect its survival. High densities occur only in rare years of very good rains, but the stress of so many animals together may inhibit reproduction for many seasons to come.

The northern brown bandicoot lives over a vast area, encompassing many different habitat types. By studying its lifestyle in each of these habitats, scientists hope to discover how the species breeds successfully in each vegetation zone. They then hope to apply this knowledge to the conservation of more endangered species of bandicoot. ∎

Illustration Steve Kingston & Kim Thompson

## NATIONAL PARKS

The national parks system of western New Guinea (Irian Jaya) was specifically designed, in the early 1980s, with the conservation of marsupials in mind. There are fifty areas in the system, with a combined total of over 31,660 sq miles (82,000 sq km). As yet, not all are fully protected, and illegal logging and forest clearance proceed in places. Nevertheless, it is a good start, especially as many protect remote areas that harbor rare and little-known species, and the parks provide a focus for study. Protected areas in Papua New Guinea are fewer but protection is generally better advanced. A number of rare, little-known, and restricted marsupials occur in them, including the giant bandicoot, which is only known from one restricted locality.

Because Australia has been more disturbed than New Guinea by human activity, it is not enough just to set up national parks there. Consequently, although all except one of the nineteen endangered and eight vulnerable marsupial species in Australia have at least part of their population within a protected area, more active management is being taken. This involves specific conservation plans for each species. Each of these may involve field studies, captive breeding, or even transferring them elsewhere.

## IUCN ACTION PLAN

*The International Union for the Conservation of Nature (IUCN) recently published an Action Plan for marsupial conservation; this sets priorities in Australia and New Guinea and makes recommendations as to how these might best be carried out. The plan identifies twenty-two species that are critically endangered and a further thirty-three about which too little is known for their conservation to be planned.*

# ZEBRAS

Stan Osolinski/Oxford Scientific Films

*Zebras and tapirs are odd-toed ungulates of the Perissodactyla order, which also includes the horse, ass, and rhino.*

**ORDER**

*Perissodactyla* (odd-toed ungulates)

**FAMILY**

*Equidae* (horses, zebras, and asses)

**GENUS**

*Equus*

**SPECIES**

*burchelli* (plains zebra)

*zebra* (mountain zebra)

*grevyi* (Grevy's zebra)

**FAMILY**

*Tapiridae* (tapirs)

**GENUS**

*Tapirus*

**SPECIES**

*terrestris* (Brazilian tapir)

*pinchaque* (mountain tapir)

*bairdi* (Baird's tapir)

*indicus* (Malayan tapir)

# HORSES IN FANCY DRESS

## ZEBRAS ARE BY FAR THE MOST EYE-CATCHING OF AFRICA'S GRAZING MAMMALS. THEIR RELATIVES THE TAPIRS ARE QUITE THE OPPOSITE, MELTING INTO THE FOREST GREENERY AT THE FIRST SIGN OF DANGER

Zebras are equids, members of the horse family. Together with horses and asses they form the six surviving species of a group that first roamed the earth some 60 million years ago and that has seen many different species in that time. Another species of zebra, the quagga, became extinct only at the end of the last century. Although a few wild horses still exist in protected areas, it is extremely doubtful that any survive in a truly wild state today.

Zebras and tapirs belong to an order of mammals known as the Perissodactyla, or odd-toed ungulates (hoofed grazers). Like asses and horses, zebras have only one visible toe on each foot, and this is bound in a tough hoof. Rather like rhinos—the only other perissodactyl family—the tapirs have three main digits on each foot, each one encased in a long hoof.

The earliest "horse" was a small, solitary forest browser known as *Eohippus* (*ee–o–HIPP–us*) or dawn horse. This round-backed animal had three

# (in)SIGHT

## EXPRESSIVE FACES

All equids have long muzzles, with deep jaws that house 40–42 constantly growing teeth. These are needed to crop and grind the quantities of grass required to sustain the animal's bulk. Ruminants, by contrast, have a more efficient digestive system, and their muzzles are correspondingly smaller. Equids also have large, powerful chewing muscles to chew the fibrous diet; this accounts for the deep lower jawbone, to which the big muscles are anchored.

Ruminants and nonruminants differ also in that the former tend to gather food with their long, muscular tongue, whereas the latter have developed mobile lips. As a result equids, with their long muzzles, big jaw muscles, rubbery lips, and mobile ears have more scope for facial expression than ruminants. The mouth, ears, and angle of the head can all be altered in an infinite number of permutations to signify mood.

Gerard Lacz/NHPA

toes on each hind foot and four on each forefoot. Over millions of years it evolved into the grazers of today; the genus *Equus* first appeared 2 million years ago. Although equids first appeared in North America, they died out there some 10,000 years ago and are found naturally only in Africa and Asia.

The modern tapir genus, *Tapirus*, first appeared some 20 million years ago, but has changed little since then. The animals we know today are among the most primitive of any of today's large mammals and, indeed, some experts claim they are remarkably similar to the common ancestors of all perissodactyls. Although they are found around the equator and in the southern hemisphere today, they originated in the northern hemisphere and were once much more widely distributed throughout Europe and North America. They have actually lived in South America only for the past 2 million years.

Although to us all zebras look fairly similar, each of the three species is in fact clearly identifiable by its stripe patterns. And within these patterns, no two zebras are ever identical; their markings are as individually unique as human fingerprints. All zebras have a mane of short, erectile hairs that extends from between the ears down the neck to the withers. Their long tail differs from that of a horse but is similar to those of asses in having a tufted tip.

*Like wild horses, plains zebras are highly sociable, living in permanent groups or harems.*

Of the three species, Grevy's is the largest—in fact it is the largest of all living wild equids and may have been the first of the modern equids to evolve. In many respects it is built like an ass, with its long, narrow head and big, broad ears—it even tends to bray like an ass. As in all zebras, the bold vertical stripes on its neck extend through its mane, which makes its neck seem even thicker than it is.

Both the plains and mountain zebras are more horselike in build. The plains zebra is noticeably stocky. Although there is a recognizable overall patterning, there is so much variety in the striping and color within this species that at one time over twenty subspecies were described. Some authorities still recognize up to five subspecies. Indeed, a fair amount of confusion surrounds this zebra. Echoing its Latin species name, it is often known as Burchell's zebra (and, less frequently, as the common or steppe zebra). A Burchell's zebra subspecies, the now extinct quagga, was also referred to as a Burchell.

The mountain zebra has one distinguishing feature—a "dewlap," or fold of skin at the throat, which is absent in the other species and seems to serve no clear purpose. It also tends to have narrow, rather rubbery hoofs that are harder and more pointed than those of the other species. This helps it on the hard ground of its rocky, arid environment; if these zebras spend a lot of time on softer ground, the feet can grow too long and become distorted. Mountain

*The Brazilian tapir is an elusive forest-dweller that browses on leafy ground cover* (above).

T. Whittaker/Frank Lane Picture Agency

zebras are generally thinner and sleeker than the plains zebras, with larger ears.

The four tapir species look nothing like zebras; they are actually more closely related to the rhinos, which diverged from the tapirs' ancestors some 40 million years ago. Like zebras, tapirs originated as forest browsers; unlike them, however, they never made the move out onto the open plains. The Brazilian, Baird's, and mountain tapir are found in the forests of Central and South America, while the Malayan tapir lives in Southeast Asia.

## THE ZEBRAS' AND TAPIRS' FAMILY TREE

*Zebras are contained in the same genus as horses and asses; in spite of their apparently common striped appearance, they are no more closely related to one another than they are to the others in the genus. Zebras may be described as being striped horses; horses as unstriped zebras. Some experts place the six species in this genus into various subgenera, but even then each zebra species is contained in its own subgenus. The four species of tapir are all contained in the same genus and are the only members of their family.*

## MOUNTAIN ZEBRA
*Equus zebra*
*(ECK-wus ZEEB-rah)*

**The smallest of the zebras, the mountain zebra is most similar in appearance to the plains zebra although it is generally sleeker and has longer ears. It is specially adapted to arid mountain ranges in its much diminished range. There are two subspecies: the Cape mountain zebra, E. z. zebra, and Hartmann's mountain zebra, E. z. hartmannae. The Cape zebra is the smaller of the two, and is also particularly rare.**

## HORSES

Tapirs look slightly like an elephant crossed with a pig. Fairly low, with short, almost slender legs, the body is very thickset and rounded, and the tapering profile to the head is emphasized by the short, fleshy trunk, or proboscis, which comprises the nose and upper lip. The trunk is shortest in the Malayan tapir, which is nevertheless the largest of the four species. Although the oval ears are not very mobile the hearing is good, while the small eyes are deep set. The short, bristly coat is at its most dense in the mountain tapir, which lives in the coldest regions. The mountain tapir has white lips and white rings around its ears, and all species have a thick, bristly mane down the back of the short neck.

The three New World species are all a red-brown color, sometimes with a white chin and white-fringed ears, whereas the Malayan tapir is boldly piebald in black and white. Tapirs are quite large, up to 95 in (240 cm) long in the case of the Malayan tapir and may weigh over 660 lb (300 kg). Stocky and solid, they are forces to be reckoned with. ∎

## GONE FOREVER

**Among zebras, the quagga probably looked most like the wild horse, although it was a subspecies of the plains zebra. Now extinct, this animal had characteristic zebra striping in a red-brown color and white on its neck and face—except for the muzzle—fading and merging over the back and body to become a solid red-brown. The belly, legs, and tail were a creamy white.**

**Vast herds once grazed the African plains, but when these areas were required for farmland, the quagga was killed by the thousands. The meat was used as food and the skins tanned for leather or made into grain sacks. The last wild quagga was shot in the Cape Province in the 1850s, while the last remaining zoo specimen died in 1883.**

Color illustrations Steve Kingston

## EQUIDS

## ODD-TOED UNGULATES

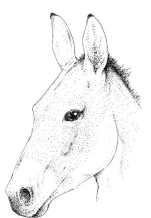

## ASSES

# GREVY'S ZEBRA

### *Equus grevyi*
*(ECK-wus GREE-vee-ie)*

Grevy's zebra has narrow flank stripes and a white underbelly. It is thought to have been the first zebra to evolve, soon after the early horses had developed the hoof or single toe, and is only distantly related to the other two species. While the plains and mountain zebras live a more or less stable, sociable life within a herd or harem on the rich subtropical grasslands, Grevy's zebra is more of a loner—especially the male—since its scrubby, dry subdesert habitat deters grazers from settling too long in one area.

# TAPIR
### *Tapirus*
*(tah-PEER-us)*

A distinctive feature of the big, bulky tapir is the short proboscis, which has nostrils placed transversely at the tip. The Malayan tapir is the biggest of all the species in terms of bulk and weight, while Baird's tapir is the largest of the three New World species. Some zoologists place the Malayan tapir in a separate genus—Acrocodia.

#### FOUR SPECIES:
BRAZILIAN OR SOUTH
AMERICAN TAPIR
MOUNTAIN TAPIR
BAIRD'S TAPIR
MALAYAN TAPIR

## RHINOS

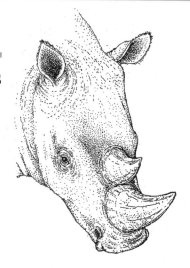

2451

# ANATOMY:
## THE
# PLAINS ZEBRA

**THE EARS**
are mobile and tapering, but small in comparison to the other zebras.

*Grevy's zebra (above left) is the largest of the zebras and of all wild equids: It reaches a maximum shoulder height of 63 in (160 cm), a head-and-body length of 118 in (300 cm) and weight of 992 lb (450 kg). The Brazilian tapir (above right) has a head-and-body length of 71–99 in (180–250 cm), a shoulder height of 30–47 in (75-120 cm) and a weight of 500–660 lb (225–300 kg).*

## STRIPE PATTERNS

The torso and head stripes are narrow over a buff or white base, while the neck stripes tend to be broad. Stripes take on a concentric pattern on the rump. The belly is white and there are two white stripes along the spine.

The forequarter stripes are narrow. A set of stripes form a "gridiron" pattern over the rump and tail. Hindquarter and flank stripes are broader. The legs are striped and the belly is white, except for a black stripe on the chest.

The broad body stripes extend under the belly; they usually continue down the legs, either to the hooves or to the fetlocks (ankles). Southerly animals are less boldly striped with fewer stripes on the belly, hindquarters, and legs.

**GREVY'S ZEBRA**

**MOUNTAIN ZEBRA**

**PLAINS ZEBRA**

**X RAY**

**ZEBRA SKULL**
*The skull is greatly elongated with long, narrow nasal bones. The eye socket is set behind the teeth so as to avoid any pressure on the eyes by the long molars. The lower jawbone is particularly big to accommodate the large cheek teeth and to serve as a broad anchorage for the chewing muscles.*

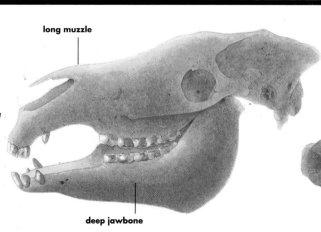

long muzzle

deep jawbone

**TEETH**
*The zebra is well equipped to deal with its diet of tough, fibrous grass. The strong incisors are used to crop the sward, and the high-crowned molars grind it efficiently.*

incisors

large molars

X-ray illustrations Elisabeth Smith

### CLASSIFICATION

**GENUS:** *EQUUS*

**SPECIES:** *BURCHELLI*

### SIZE

**HEIGHT TO SHOULDER:** 49–53 IN (125–135 CM)

**HEAD–BODY LENGTH:** 83–102 IN (210–260 CM)

**TAIL LENGTH:** 16–22 IN (40–55 CM)

### COLORATION

BROAD, VERTICAL BLACK AND WHITE STRIPES ON BODY AND DOWN CENTER OF FACE, BECOMING ALMOST HORIZONTAL ON THE SIDES OF THE FACE, HAUNCHES, AND LEGS

### FEATURES

FAIRLY SMALL, NEAT HEAD

COMPACT, WELL-PROPORTIONED BODY CHARACTERIZED BY SLEEK ROUNDNESS ON BELLY AND HINDQUARTERS

LEGS SHORTER THAN IN GREVY'S ZEBRA, GIVING A DUMPIER APPEARANCE

## THE MANE

is a scrubby, erect crest of hairs extending from between the ears to the withers (base of the neck). Stripes continue into the mane, but the core hairs are black.

## THE BODY

is rather dumpy in appearance, and plains zebras tend to appear overweight.

## THE FEET

have a single toe, in which the nail has developed into a horny, protective outer wall, known as the hoof.

## THE TAIL

is long, with horizontal black and white stripes ending in a tuft of long dark and pale intermingling hairs. There is a black line down the center.

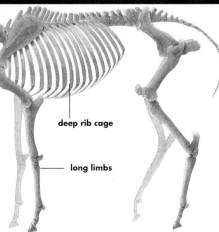

## SKELETON
The long spine is almost straight compared with the markedly more arched, convex spine of primitive species, such as the tapirs. Combined with the deep rib cage, which gives plenty of room for lungs, and the long limbs, this gives speed and stamina for sustained galloping.

deep rib cage

long limbs

## TAPIR SKULL
This is relatively short and narrow. The nasal bones are short and arched, the long "trunk" solely comprising tissue and muscle, not elongated bone. Tapirs have the same number of teeth as equids but they are relatively smaller, and the cheek teeth are particularly low-crowned.

short, domed skull

small, low-crowned molars

Main illustrations Kim Thompson

# BLACK AND WHITE

**ALTHOUGH THEY SHARE A COMMON ANCESTRY AND ARE CLASSIFIED IN THE SAME ORDER, ZEBRAS AND TAPIRS LEAD COMPLETELY DIFFERENT LIVES—FROM THEIR CHOICE OF HABITAT TO THEIR DAILY HABITS**

Art Wolfe/Tony Stone Images

Most facets of their behavior suggest that zebras and tapirs lead almost diametrically opposed lifestyles. By and large, tapirs are shy and solitary animals spending their lives in the cover of dense forest, seeking the company of another tapir only at breeding time. They further their desire to be alone and elusive by being active almost only at night. Zebras, by contrast, are creatures of the wide-open African grasslands, with striking coat patterns that make them as conspicuous as any of the plains grazers. They are also among the most sociable of animals, grazing in mixed herds that may contain gnu, springbok, gazelles, various other types of antelope, elk, giraffes, buffalo—even elephants.

In one element of their behavior, zebras and tapirs are alike: They spend most of their active hours feeding, whether it be a nightly or daily activity. The similarity ends with that, for tapirs are mainly browsers—although they do also nibble on grass when it suits them. They tend also to be almost constantly on the go, stopping at a bush only to pluck a few mouthfuls of foliage before moving quickly on. Zebras are consummate grazers, browsing on leaves only very occasionally. As their daytime activity begins, they wander from their overnight resting spot to the current pasture. Here they may spend most of the day, spreading out from the others in a herd, but eating constantly and systematically.

## FEEDING NICHES

The key to the contrast in the lifestyles of tapirs and zebras lies in the demands of their different feeding niches, for which they are perfectly adapted. The forest floor terrain is clearly unsuitable for herds of animals. Movement is most effective along familiar, well-worn trails with escape routes into the densest, darkest thickets when danger approaches. When

threatened, tapirs can move with surprising rapidity; they may look bulky, but their speed and streamlined shape enable them to cut a swath through the concealing ground cover of the forest. A taller animal—such as a zebra—would find it hard to follow suit.

Other aspects of the tapir's comical appearance are, in fact, evolutionary adaptations for this solitary forest lifestyle. The strange proboscis provides an excellent sense of smell but is also useful as a probe for investigating unfamiliar objects and as a tool to bring sprays of foliage within reach of the mouth.

T. Whittaker/Frank Lane Picture Agency

*Mud, mud, glorious mud: A Brazilian tapir and her offspring enjoy a cool wallow* (above).

## AMAZING FACTS

● The tapir can not only move at high speed through the forest undergrowth when necessary: It is also a good swimmer. An 18th-century naturalist classified the Brazilian tapir as *Hippopotamus terrestris*, believing it to be a species of hippo. He may have seen one wallowing in the mud, in the manner of a hippo; tapirs cool themselves by sinking into a water hole and wallow in mud pools in order to get rid of skin parasites.

● The fact that tapirs are found in both Southeast Asia and South America led early zoologists to a belief that these two continents were once joined by a land bridge—despite the fact that they have no other mammal in common.

The deep-set eyes are well protected from thorns or sharp twigs that are a feature of dense forest undergrowth and that perpetually scratch and scar the tapir's hide. The zebra's high-set, protruding eyes are more vulnerable in this respect but they do give excellent all-around vision—a vital asset on the treacherous savanna. And while the zebra's stripes are rather doubtful as a camouflage strategy there is no doubt that the striking markings of the Malayan tapir provide it with excellent concealment in the dappled light of its jungle home.

### RISKY BUSINESS

The zebra does not chew the cud like the ruminating herbivores, so it cannot rest in the shadows or long grasses and "recycle" its food but must instead stay in the more open areas, grazing almost continuously through its waking hours in order to find enough food. As such, it is a "sitting target" continuously at risk from the grassland predators—lions and hunting dogs in particular. Wandering constantly alone along the same set of paths or tracks, tapir style, would obviously invite predation, but the zebra makes virtually no attempt at concealment; instead it has adopted a "safety in numbers" strategy. Sticking close to dozens of other zebras does, at least, reduce the individual's chances of being the unlucky victim of an attack. Should it find itself in trouble, however, the zebra has further defenses for its open-plan lifestyle—such as keen senses, a hefty kick, and an impressive turn of speed. ∎

*Talking loud and clear: A warning whinny alerts a plains zebra herd to potential danger.*

# HABITATS

A heat haze settles over the sprawling grasslands of Africa's Serengeti. Enormous herds of mixed animals—wildebeest, gazelles, and zebras—begin to amass, fidgeting restlessly and snorting into the still air. Eventually the herd, which may number up to half a million animals, rolls into motion. The zebras alternate their role, first traveling at the head and flanks of the huge group, then acting as the pathfinders. The vast migration of grazers, headed for the Masai Mara Reserve in Kenya, more than 124 miles (200 kilometers) away, has begun.

Among the equids, zebras as a whole occupy one of the world's richest grass-producing habitats; the wild horse and ass species, by contrast, occur naturally in arid steppes and even desert borders. In spite of its apparent lushness, however, most zebra country is subject to seasonal shortages of grazing because of the annual dry season. This necessitates seasonal migrations of varying distances.

### DRYLAND DAZZLERS

The most widespread of zebras now is the plains zebra, still found from southern Ethiopia and Sudan south through to central Angola and eastern South Africa. Possibly the secret of its success, compared to the other two species, is that it is the most adaptable of grazers and will flourish equally in savanna, light woodland, and open scrubland. The savanna may comprise a short growth of grass and no trees, or it may feature tall grassland and scattered woodland—the plains zebra is happy with either. It may even be found in rocky, hilly country and on mountain slopes up to elevations of 14,435 ft (4,400 m). The one essential condition for the plains zebra, however, is the availability of fresh water, for it needs to drink regularly. Clearly it feels at home near water, for this zebra has been observed swimming in rivers in the wild.

The plains zebra will occasionally overlap with Grevy's zebra in the northernmost part of its range. Grevy's zebra is greatly reduced in numbers from former times and is almost entirely confined to northern Kenya—possibly extending into southeastern Ethiopia and maybe Somalia, although it may actually be extinct there. Its ideal ecological niche is subdesert, falling between areas favored by the water-dependent plains zebra and the significantly arid region farther north that is home to the African wild ass.

As its name suggests, the mountain zebra is truly adapted to upland conditions, although, strangely, the plains zebra is occasionally found at higher elevations in parts of its range. Subdesert plains, rocky slopes, and often barren plateaus in the mountainous areas of southwestern Angola, Namibia, and western South Africa are home to the mountain

*The lush, forested banks of the Aguarico River in Ecuador are home to the secretive Brazilian tapir.*

KEY

TAPIRS

GREVY'S ZEBRA

MOUNTAIN ZEBRA

PLAINS ZEBRA

*A herd of plains zebra seek out water on the open grasslands of Serengeti National Park* (left).

zebra and it is much more agile and surefooted than the other species on steep slopes. Once widespread along the dry mountain ranges that run parallel to the coast from southern Angola to the Transvaal, the mountain zebra—particularly the Cape subspecies—is sadly reduced in numbers. It is found up to heights of 6,560 ft (2,000 m), but will frequently descend to lower elevations after rainfall, extending into the desert and coastal dunes, to slake its thirst at replenished water holes.

Although less water-dependent than the plains zebra, mountain zebras nevertheless need to drink at least once, sometimes twice a day in the hot dry season. Both the mountain and Grevy's zebra have been seen using their front hooves to dig for subsurface water in dry streambeds. Having exposed a supply in a small pit, they will fiercely defend it from other grazing animals, even from members of their own herd. If necessary, Grevy's and mountain zebras can exist on fairly brackish water.

### FOREST AND SWAMP

The Malayan tapir is a denizen of the dense primary rain forests, both lowland and highland, of southern Burma and Thailand, Malaysia, and Sumatra. It may also occur in Laos. On the island of Sumatra it is only found to the south of Lake Toba in the northern part. This huge lake appears to mark a boundary for several rain-forest species, which are found only to the south of this point.

---

**AFTER THE DOMESTIC HORSE, THE PLAINS ZEBRA IS THE MOST SUCCESSFUL EQUID IN TERMS OF DISTRIBUTION**

---

At one time, tapirs were considerably more widespread in Southeast Asia; in prehistoric times they were found on the other Sunda Islands, Java and Borneo. A giant form was also found in China. Tapirs have disappeared from some of these areas since the evolution of man and it is thought he may have overhunted it even in those earlier times.

The Malayan tapir has a liking for low-lying swampy areas and is at least partly aquatic in habit; it will remain submerged in water for hours on end. Its short legs make easy work of steep, rocky inclines. Active mainly in the hours of darkness, it travels around a limited area using the same paths night after night, reducing them to swampy ruts.

The Brazilian tapir has the largest range in South America, extending from east of the Colombian Andes and Venezuela south to northern

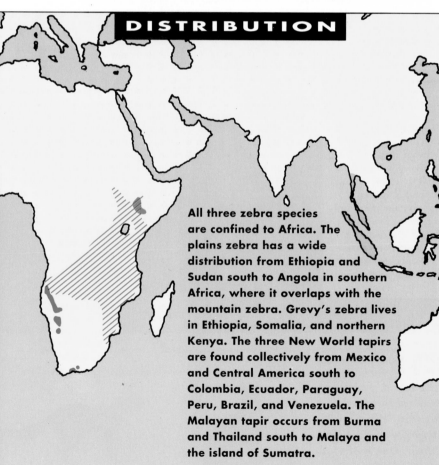

## DISTRIBUTION

**All three zebra species are confined to Africa. The plains zebra has a wide distribution from Ethiopia and Sudan south to Angola in southern Africa, where it overlaps with the mountain zebra. Grevy's zebra lives in Ethiopia, Somalia, and northern Kenya. The three New World tapirs are found collectively from Mexico and Central America south to Colombia, Ecuador, Paraguay, Peru, Brazil, and Venezuela. The Malayan tapir occurs from Burma and Thailand south to Malaya and the island of Sumatra.**

Argentina and southern Brazil. Its swimming prowess is frequently called into account, for its range is laced with rivers, but it is also found in the dry deciduous forest of the Chaco Plains of Argentina. It, too, moves along habitual paths, often entering-and leaving rivers by the same path each time.

Baird's tapir, the largest of the three New World species, is the only species to be found in Central America, extending south from Mexico to Colombia and Ecuador, west of the Andes. At one time, tapirs were widespread through North America and were present in the Florida Peninsula until about 11,000 years ago—roughly the same time that equids disappeared from northern America. Tapirs probably migrated into South America from North America, in search of a more amenable environment.

Baird's tapir prefers mainly lowland swampy or hilly forests. Like the Malayan tapir, it is primarily nocturnal. Agile like all tapirs, it negotiates very steep cliffs and awkward terrain, including limestone cliffs, with ease and speed, once more repeatedly using the same tracks.

The mountain tapir has the smallest distribution of the New World species and is an inhabitant of the high elevations of the Andes Mountains in Colombia and Ecuador. Never found lower than altitudes of 6,560 ft (2,000 m), it is equally at home

as high as 14,765 ft (4,500 m), above the tree line. It may also be seen grazing at the evergreen grasslands below the snow line.

Possessing the same agility and hill-climbing ability that typifies all tapirs, the mountain tapir is further equipped for the colder climes of its environment in being more compact, which enables it to conserve body heat more efficiently. It also has a dense coat of hair, which comprises a thick underfur and a long-haired outercoat, protecting it from the freezing nighttime temperatures. ∎

## FOCUS ON

Planet Earth Pictures

### TROPICAL FORESTS OF BURMA, THAILAND, AND MALAYSIA

**Nearly three-fifths of Burma is covered by forest, while more than half of the land surface of Thailand and the Malay Peninsula is also covered with trees.**

In Burma, the eastern mountain system separates Burma from Thailand, Laos, and China; the western mountain belt is a region of thick forests along the border between Burma and India, and the fertile central belt is irrigated by the Irrawaddy River. In the north of Thailand lie mountains covered with thick evergreen forests; to the south lies the central plain, where rice is grown. The southern peninsula consists mainly of tropical forest.

The forests in these areas have some of the richest animal and plant life of anywhere in the world. In Burma there are elephants, tigers, leopards, gibbons, monkeys, gaurs and bantengs, and the very rare Asian two-horned rhino. There are more than a thousand bird species and many reptiles, including vipers, crocodiles, turtles, and a variety of lizards. Thailand's forests have many of the same animals as well as a proliferation of wild boars and poisonous snakes such as banded kraits and cobras.

## TEMPERATURE AND RAINFALL

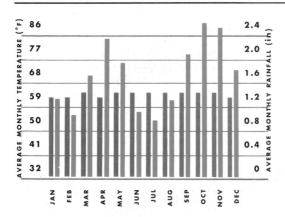

■ **TEMPERATURE**

■ **RAINFALL**

*These areas have a subtropical and/or tropical climate. Thailand is typical with three seasons: a hot dry spring, a hot wet summer, and a mild winter. From July to December is the monsoon season; in Burma this runs from May to October.*

### NEIGHBORS

**The warm, moist tropical forests are blessed with a huge diversity of flora and fauna: One-half of all living species reside in the equatorial belt of rain forests that once encircled the globe.**

**LEOPARD**

*Abundantly equipped with feline hunting skills, the leopard is one of the tapir's principal enemies.*

**DHOLE**

*The dhole also preys on the Malayan tapir. A tireless hunter, it pursues its quarry either alone or in packs.*

Neighbor illustrations Richard Tibbits

**BURMA, THAILAND, AND MALAYSIA**

*These three densely forested countries lie across the equatorial belt. The area now known as Malaysia was formed as late as 1963 when Malaya, Singapore, and the islands of Sabah and Sarawak united.*

**TAPIR RANGE**

**MALAYAN CIVET**

The catlike Malayan civet is actually related to the mongoose. Like the tapir, it is chiefly nocturnal.

**GAUR**

This massive bovid is found in tropical forests across India, Indochina, and the Malay Peninsula.

**BEARDED PIG**

This stocky wild pig lives in mangrove swamps and open woodlands as well as dense tropical forest.

**SIAMANG**

One of the forest's noisiest inhabitants, the siamang is a gibbon of Southeast Asia's highland tropical forests.

**SLOW LORIS**

This tree-dwelling primate has huge, sensitive eyes specially adapted for night vision in the dark forest.

# FOOD AND FEEDING

All tapirs are principally browsers, cruising around familiar forest tracks, usually on a zigzag course to confuse predators. As they move, they keep their snout low to the ground, for smell is a very important sense to these animals.

Selecting succulent vegetation, tapirs feed on aquatic plants, leaves, twigs, new green shoots, and fruit from low bushes. Ferns and bamboos feature in the mountain tapir's diet, as its habitat is dominated by stunted plant growth. Having found a suitable shrub, a tapir does not strip it bare; instead it plucks only a mouthful or two and then moves on. In this way it is constantly on the move, watchful rather than engrossed in feeding.

The tapir's fleshy trunk plays a key role in feeding. First it sniffs out succulent vegetation, then it uses its mobile lips to pluck the morsel. The tapir's teeth suit its feeding habits: The low-crowned molars have a series of ridges and cusps to help grind the food. Every now and then, a tapir reverts to grazing, cropping the blades of grass with its sharp incisors.

At night, a tapir feeds constantly. It favors forest clearings and grassy glades, as well as riverbanks; the water provides a refuge if danger threatens. Besides vegetation, tapirs love salt; in national parks in Malaysia, they will travel great distances to reach artificial salt licks provided for them.

Zebras have a distinct advantage over many other African plains grazers in being able to consume tougher, more fibrous grasses, and this allows animals of different species to feed together. Zebras favor many of the same grasses as the grazing antelope, for example, but their different diet precludes them from direct competition. Often the zebras are the first to wander into the taller pastures, cropping the long, tough grass stems and opening up the way for other animals.

### FLEXIBLE GRAZERS

Zebras' feeding patterns vary according to the local grazing and also the weather. Usually a herd moves from nighttime resting grounds to a chosen pasture; here they may join other animals, but tend to fan out, cropping each patch fully before moving on a few steps. They may rest at midday, taking a cool dust bath or grooming one another. Toward dusk they return to the resting area. A herd may travel some 10.5 miles (17 km) in a day's grazing activities.

In times of drought or during the drier seasons, zebras may join other animals to migrate across the plains in search of lush grass. This is particularly

*Water can be scarce on the savanna, and grazers take full advantage of any flash rainfalls* (right).

Illustrations Robin Budden/Wildlife Art Agency

### LAWN MOWERS

*Zebras spend the day feeding intensively, moving slowly from one patch of grass to the next* (above).

M. Harvey/Natural Science Photos

### *in* SIGHT

## CAPABLE CROPPERS

The skull and dentition of zebras, as with other equids, have changed through time to enable them to deal with the tough, fibrous, often razor-sharp blades of grass that are the mainstay of their diet. The incisors—three on either side of the upper and lower jaws—are long and sharp and act like pincers, slicing off the grasses at whatever point the zebra chooses.

The molars and premolars—again, three of each in either side of the top and bottom jaw—have developed in a similar fashion, becoming large, almost four-cornered and flat on top, making them superb crushing and grinding tools. They are high-crowned and possess vertical layers of enamel sandwiched between two harder areas of ivory and cement. This reduces wear and tear, which would make these teeth dull and blunt and ultimately useless in chewing.

Zebras basically have no need of the sharp canine teeth, usually used for piercing flesh; male stallions alone grow canine teeth, which they use in fighting.

### SNIFF AND GRAB

*Tapirs first seek out tasty morsels with their fine sense of smell, then use their rubbery, mobile lips to reach out and pluck the food* (left).

the pattern of the plains zebra, which may travel hundreds of miles in the course of the year. Mountain zebras tend to move to higher elevations in dry months, following paths that they know lead to constant watering places and certain, if poor, grazing. Grevy's zebra is possibly the least migratory, apparently better able to resist drought conditions than the plains zebra. It subsists on poor grass and digs out water holes in dusty, dried-up riverbeds with its hooves. In such conditions, it survives but its breeding rate tends to drop. ∎

# DEFENSES

**B**oth zebras and tapirs are prey to some of the most accomplished of carnivores. On the plains, a zebra makes a hearty meal for a pride of lions, or a pack of hyenas or hunting dogs. In the jungles of Southeast Asia, the tiger and leopard are more than a match for the ponderous tapir, while its New World relatives are the prey of jaguars.

A tapir is poorly equipped to deal with predators, hence its more cautious lifestyle. It is alerted to the presence of an enemy by its keen sense of smell and hearing, and the slightest whiff of trouble signifies the cue to flee: The tapir either bolts through the dense undergrowth, hoping to give its pursuer the slip, or takes refuge in the water if near enough to a river. Tapirs often sleep on a riverbank, and it is here that they are particularly vulnerable.

### DEFENSIVE CAMOUFLAGE

One of the tapir's chief defenses is its coloring. The red-brown coat and pale underside of the three New World species helps them to merge in with their often dingy habitats. The striking black-and-white coloration of the Malayan tapir provides surprisingly good camouflage in the bold shadows of its often more brightly lit jungle home. Baby tapirs are born with coats that are marked with white spots and stripes, helping to camouflage them in the shaded, dappled undergrowth until they are better able to protect themselves. Baird's and Brazilian tapirs, in particular, have a short, thick mane which may give some protection at the base of the neck—a key target for the jaguar's deadly canines. Although all tapirs undoubtedly adopt a policy of flight when danger threatens, if they find themselves cornered they will defend themselves to the best of their ability by biting. Their bulk and size means that they are formidable opponents to all but the most efficient and determined of predators.

### THE USE OF STRIPES

That zebras are compelled to live their lives in the full glare of the African plains—where fast-running, stealthy predators are ever on the lookout for a substantial meal—means that they must be well equipped to defend themselves. Many people have attempted to attribute camouflage properties to their striped coats—the stripes echoing the long grass, or confusing a predator by blurring the zebra's outline, particularly in the heat haze that often settles over the terrain. There may be some truth in these suggestions, although other experts also point out that a striped coat pattern is not found in other plains prey animals—wildebeests, for example, with which zebras often coexist and which have to contend with the same predators.

Plains zebras are first alerted to the presence of predators in a number of ways; often a herd will have a lookout—an animal or animals intent on

NHPA

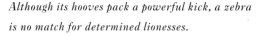

*Although its hooves pack a powerful kick, a zebra is no match for determined lionesses.*

form part of a mixed herd that includes zebras, and many people say these large, flightless birds make particularly good lookouts.

Zebras themselves have acute senses of hearing and smell, which means they will often be the ones to spot a predator. In addition, evolution has pushed their eye sockets high up on their heads, in order to make room for the roots of the massive cheek teeth. The vision of equids is such that they can graze while also scanning the surrounding area for movement. Their only blind spot lies directly behind them, and they are particularly vulnerable when drinking at a water hole.

Once alerted to the presence of predators, plains zebras react in a distinctive manner. The herd stands in a close circle or corral, with foals on the inside, to observe the predator—a resting lion, or perhaps a pack of hunting dogs. If the predators are on the move, the zebras will make way for them, still maintaining their tight formation. If the adversary is a wandering lion, the zebras may suddenly gallop across its path, apparently testing if it is out to tackle one of them. If the lion does not follow, the zebras come to a halt, still watching it. If the lion chases them, they will flee in a tight bunch, with the stallion—the strongest member of the group—to the rear. Healthy, adult zebras are generally able to outrun their predators.

If necessary, a zebra stallion will attack predators, lashing out with its hind legs; a well-aimed blow from these is able to smash the skull of a hunting dog or inflict serious injury on a lion. The canine

---

IN DEFENSE, ZEBRAS EITHER KICK OUT WITH THE FORE- OR HIND FEET, OR, AS A LAST RESORT, BITE THEIR ENEMIES

---

teeth of zebra stallions are sharp and pointed (unlike those of the mares) and stallions have been known to seize an attacking hyena in their mouths and fling it through the air. Sometimes simply charging at a pack of hyenas, with head lowered, ears pressed back in aggression, and teeth bared, is sufficient to deter these voracious predators.

Inevitably, all zebras do not escape predation, however well equipped they are to do so. In flight, it will usually be young, old, or weak animals that fall victim to pursuing predators. To some extent this actually benefits zebras by weeding out infirm animals that might otherwise slow up the herd and put it at further risk. ∎

### CLEAR OFF!

*Head down, teeth bared, and nostrils snorting, a stallion sees off a hyena that has crept too close to his harem*
(below).

scanning the horizon while the others graze. A large, mixed herd will obviously have more of a chance of spotting predators early; grazing animals of all kinds are always on the lookout and are easily alerted. Many, including zebras, have a "special relationship" with oxpeckers; these little birds sit on the backs of the grazing animals removing and feeding on the ticks from their coats. From their vantage point they can spot approaching predators, and will invariably trill a warning. Ostriches also sometimes

2463

# SOCIAL STRUCTURE

Shy, solitary tapirs display little in the way of social structure. They are territorial to the extent of marking the pathways they habitually use through their home range with urine and dung. Accumulated heaps of dung, scraped up by the tapir, warn neighboring tapirs not to intrude on marked feeding areas. The fact that tapirs habitually move with their snouts close to the ground is an indication that they are anxious to detect the scent of others. If tapirs meet on a foraging route, they tend to react aggressively, showing their displeasure with shrill whistles. They approach one another with teeth bared and, if one does not retreat, they may begin fighting by circling each other and snapping at each other's legs.

The tapir's strong territorial instinct is to defend its food source; it has no desire to roam farther afield in search of fresh food, since by browsing lightly it preserves the resources within its established area. Zebras, on the other hand, have no need to defend a food source; not only are grasses plentiful, but the nature of their habitat, which supports many grazing animals, would make such a defense almost impossible. In the main, zebras tend toward a sociable lifestyle, although Grevy's zebra behaves in a different manner from the other two species.

The basic social unit among Grevy's zebras is that of a mare with her young—the latest foal plus possibly those of the previous years. Often such a unit will unite with other mares and their offspring, particularly if there is a migration to richer pastures. At such times forty or more mares may form a group. More usually however, these mares number about ten, but even then such groups are not stable; mares tolerate one another's presence but owe one another no allegiance. They will move from one group to another as conditions suit them alone.

### BACHELOR PARTIES

Young bachelor Grevy's zebras tend to form herds of up to ten animals. Adults of six years or more maintain territories, purely for mating purposes. As females pass through the territory toward fresh pastures, the resident male seeks out those that are sexually receptive, then tries to herd them and mate with them. Territories are usually 2–4 sq miles (5–10 sq km). A stallion will tolerate the presence of bachelor herds within the territory, provided that they do not try to mate with any mares that pass through.

Territories defended by Grevy's zebra stallions are the largest of any herbivore. They mark boundaries

### IN THE HAREM

*Plains zebras live in a tight-knit herd, which is led by a stallion. He defends his mares and their young from enemies. He also fends off rival males (below). Subordinate "bachelor" males gather on the sidelines, hoping to take over their own harem someday.*

# *in*SIGHT

## WHY THE STRIPES?

It seems likely that the ancestors of equids were striped, so we may well wonder why the zebras have kept these stripes while the horse and asses have lost them. The idea of stripes affording camouflage has largely been rejected: Certainly, all zebras make no attempt to hide when predators are near. It has been suggested that the stripes protect against troublesome tsetse flies, which appear to be more attracted to solid coat colors, but these are not a hazard over the greater part of zebras' ranges.

It is most likely that stripes aid recognition, especially among mares and their foals and also between members of a group or a species. Each species has its own stripe pattern on the hindquarters, which may help during migrations. The stripes may also be an aid to grooming, indicating favored spots. For example, equids often groom one another at the base of the neck, and the stripes are usually boldest at this point. Very few abnormal patterns occur in zebras; when they do, animals seem to have trouble settling into a social group.

Illustration Wildlife Art Agency

Mark Newman/Frank Lane Picture Agency

*Herd members groom one another regularly during the day. They also swat flies from one another's faces, using their tufted tails.*

with piles of dung and urinate at key sites. Other males can be seen sniffing at these, then lifting their heads and curling their lips in response.

### WINNING A HAREM

The social behavior of plains and mountain zebras is nonterritorial; it revolves instead around the stallion and his harem of mares. This grouping is common among wild or feral horses, but somewhat less common among other mammals. A stallion establishes his herd by abducting young fillies (females) from their parental herd. Often he meets with opposition from the resident stallion, and the two fight it out. Rarely are really serious injuries inflicted; the vanquished is quick to recognize his status.

A challenge from a bachelor to a resident stallion is usually in order to abduct a filly, rather than an attempt to usurp his supremacy as head of the herd. Although fillies do get taken in this way, a resident stallion will, in true style, put up a spirited fight in order to show his fitness as head of a herd. Usually a stallion retains possession of his mares for some time, only being replaced when he is either badly injured or too old to fight. At such a time a bachelor stallion may shadow the herd, gradually pushing the old stallion out rather than actively challenging him to a fight. Even then it may take some time for the mares to accept him as the new leader.

A herd stallion not only defends his mares from bachelor stallions—like Grevy's zebras, these will usually associate in small groups—but will also herd them together and protect them from predators. A mare will lead the flight away from danger, with the stallion staying at the back ready to attack the predator if necessary. ■

# REPRODUCTION

Female zebras are receptive every few weeks, but births are generally timed to coincide with the rainy season, when grass is most abundant. Since gestation takes roughly a year, mating also occurs at this time. It suits the zebra herd to foal in unison, as lone foals are so vulnerable to predators. Despite this, however, births among plains zebras seem to continue at a peak for about six months.

In plains and mountain zebras, a herd stallion identifies the receptive mares by sniffing at their urine. It may be a few days before the mare is fully receptive, during which time the two will indulge in nibbling and mutual grooming. Mating is generally repeated every few hours over a 24-hour period. In Grevy's zebra, where a stallion mates with mares as they cross his territory, the courtship may be violent. The stallion herds the mare by chasing and nipping her, and repeatedly tries to mount her; if she is not ready she lashes out with her hooves.

Zebras give birth to a single foal lying down, often in the open. In the case of the plains and mountain zebras, the herd is generally nearby, with the stallion being highly vigilant. In Grevy's zebras, birth is a more solitary affair. Grevy's zebra foals are usually brown and black with a crest of longer hairs extending right down the body to the tail. Adult coloration develops at about four months of age.

A foal is up on its feet within about ten minutes, breaking the umbilical cord as it rises. The mare licks its anus to encourage it to defecate. Within an hour the foal is walking, and shortly afterward can trot and canter after the mare.

Initially, newborn foals are so leggy that they have to splay their forelimbs to reach the ground, but they grow into proportion. They are playful, particularly the colt (male) foals. Later on, bachelor herds of young males spend a lot of time indulging in mock fights and general "horseplay," presumably rehearsing for when fighting will be more important to establish their adult role.

Foals stay reasonably close to the mare, however, for some time, and are weaned at about eight to ten months old, even though they have been nibbling grass since about a week after their birth. Young males generally leave a herd at two to

Illustrations Robin Boutell/Wildlife Art Agency

**RIVALRY FIGHTS**

*between stallions look very violent, although bloodshed is usually avoided. The biting, hoof-pounding, and whinnying unsettle the herd, until eventually the victor drives away his adversary and claims his "ownership" of the females* (below).

## A PATTERN FOR SURVIVAL

*Unlike the zebra's stripes, those of a tapir are designed to conceal and protect the tiny offspring.*

three years old, teaming up with others of the same age. Fillies usually stay with the herd until abducted by a stallion. Mares begin to come into season when they are a year or two old but generally do not begin breeding for another year. Stallions are five or six years old before they begin forming a herd of their own and mating successfully.

### TAPIR REPRODUCTION

Tapirs, too, can reproduce year-round but may well time births to coincide with the monsoon rains. Males track down receptive females by their scent, and courtship is a noisy affair with lots of wheezes and whistles. Mating is accompanied by biting and sometimes occurs in the water. After this point the male loses interest in the female, and she gives birth to a single young after 55–59 weeks. The baby is small but well formed, with eyes already open. The female licks it to encourage it to stand, at which time she lies on her side and nudges it toward her teats. For a week or so the baby lies low in the bushes, later accompanying its mother on her foraging trips. Its baby coat of white stripes and spots begins to fade at about five months old, and by the time it is ten months it has its full adult coloration. Soon after, it leaves its mother. ■

*Born in the open, the Grevy's zebra foal must be able to run with its mother within hours of birth. It suckles for up to eleven months, growing rapidly on her rich milk (below).*

### FROM BIRTH TO DEATH

| PLAINS ZEBRA | MALAYAN TAPIR |
|---|---|
| **GESTATION:** 360–396 DAYS | **GESTATION:** 390–403 DAYS |
| **NUMBER OF YOUNG:** 1 | **NUMBER OF YOUNG:** 1 |
| **WEANED:** 8–11 MONTHS | **WEANED:** NOT KNOWN |
| **INDEPENDENCE:** 2–3 YEARS | **INDEPENDENCE:** 10–11 MONTHS |
| **SEXUAL MATURITY:** 4–6 YEARS IN MALES; 3 YEARS IN FEMALES | **SEXUAL MATURITY:** 3–4 YEARS |
| **LONGEVITY:** UP TO 40 YEARS IN CAPTIVITY; SELDOM MORE THAN 10 YEARS IN THE WILD | **LONGEVITY:** 35 YEARS IN CAPTIVITY; NOT KNOWN IN THE WILD |

E. Dragesco/Ardea

# PATTERNED AND PROUD

## ALTHOUGH PLAINS ZEBRAS STILL THRONG THE SAVANNAS, OTHER SPECIES ARE REDUCED TO A FRACTION OF THEIR ORIGINAL NUMBERS. THE TAPIRS, TOO, ARE BELEAGUERED BY THE MARCH OF HUMANKIND

The African continent was once a paradise on earth for wildlife. For centuries huge herds of grazers coexisted with the tribal bushmen who hunted these animals only when they needed food or clothing. The arrival of the white settlers was ultimately to change the look of the landscape and, with it, seal the fate of many of the wild animals.

We have already seen how the quagga was wiped out in the last century. It was slaughtered by the Boers to free the land for domestic livestock and also to feed the local labor hired by the new settlers. It is now known that the quagga was a subspecies of the much more common Burchell's zebra and is more recently named *Equus burchelli quagga*. DNA from dried tissue on a century-old quagga hide helped clarify this taxonomic placement. A few quaggas were to survive their wild contemporaries in zoos, but these turn-of-the-century collections were not managed with the modern eye for species conservation.

Sadly, humans are slow to learn from their mistakes, for both Grevy's and the mountain zebra have declined hugely. Competition with domestic livestock and traditional game hunting has made serious inroads into zebra populations, while the striped hide has an obvious value to the pelt trade; the narrow stripes of Grevy's zebra have been particularly valued.

Extensive hunting of Grevy's zebra took place as recently as the 1970s, and the species was exterminated in many of its former strongholds. Drought has further afflicted populations, for while Grevy's zebra can cope with arid conditions, it preserves its energy by not breeding. In the 1970s in Kenya there were some 14,000 Grevy's zebras; two decades later there may be only half this number.

The mountain zebra has fared little better, despite its more remote habitat. The Cape subspecies was once common in the mountains of Cape Province in South Africa. It was among the first of the game animals to be given legal protection—although this never deterred the poachers or colonial hunters in the early 19th century. By the 1930s fewer than fifty wild Cape zebras remained. Stricter controls and the establishment of the Mountain Zebra National Park have now given the species a reprieve from extinction.

The other subspecies, Hartmann's mountain zebra, has fared a little better although its numbers have also declined in recent decades. In the 1950s it was common from southwestern Angola, over the mountains of western Namibia to the borders of South Africa, with 50,000–75,000 animals across this region. But these zebras were also persecuted, nominally to clear the land for agriculture, and recent estimates put their population at 7,000–13,000.

Karl Switak/NHPA

*The Cape mountain zebra* (above) *is today making a slow recovery from losses inflicted by hunting.*

Nick Gordon/Survival Anglia

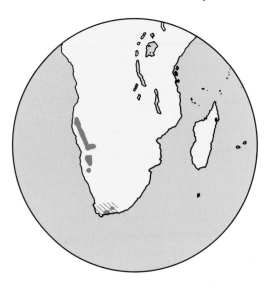

## THEN & NOW

*This map shows the former and current ranges of the mountain zebra in southern Africa.*

░░░ **FORMER**          ▓ **CURRENT**

**The two subspecies of mountain zebra are found in mountainous areas of southern Africa, including Angola, Namibia, and Cape Province. The Cape mountain zebra received protection in 1656, although this was unofficially waived by British colonials, who took control of the region in the early 19th century. The Cape zebra slumped to an ultimate low of fifty in the late 1930s but has since made a cautious recovery.**

Although the plains zebra is abundant—at least in comparison with the other two species—its range is much reduced. Farming is chiefly to blame, but hunters and poachers also take their toll. However, its numbers are still strong: 200,000 individuals in the Tanzanian Serengeti, and 5,000 or more in the Ngorongoro Crater of the Great Rift Valley.

### THREATS TO TAPIRS

The tapir has never been hunted to such a degree; but then it has always existed in far lower densities. Certainly, tapirs have been hunted for food, for their thick hide, and also for sport, particularly with the development of powerful torches and the availability of cheap guns. In Malaysia, however, the tapir is left unharmed by Muslim communities.

*In the 18th century, so many zebras were shot that paid hunters were instructed to retrieve their lead bullets from the carcasses to be melted down.*

Silvestris/Frank Lane Picture Agency

Far and away the greatest threat to tapirs in all of their ranges is the loss of habitat, for they live in the tropical rain forest. In Malaysia, colossal farming projects were sponsored by the federal government in the 1950s in an attempt to reduce unemployment. Hundreds of thousands of acres of rain forests were razed and oil palm trees planted; settler families were brought in to reap the harvest.

Much of Malaysia's rain forest has also been lost to logging. By 1983, some two-thirds of lowland forests on the Malay Peninsula had been felled to fuel the timber trade, as well as for rubber and oil palm plantations. The commercial logging companies are simply moving on to other forests in Burma, Thailand, and Indonesia—all home to the tapir.

In South America, tapirs face similar threats, as well as constant erosion of the rain forest by "slash-and-burn" agriculture. Severe poverty drives families into the rain forest, where they clear a small plot of land in the hope of growing grain. The soil is poor, however, and the families must move on, destroying ever more forest.

Perhaps surprisingly, the Brazilian tapir, living in one of the worst-hit areas of rain forest, is still the most widespread and locally abundant. Its habitat is fragmented, however, forcing it into population "pockets" that face poor breeding possibilities. Baird's tapir faces similar fragmentation and has already died out in some areas—El Salvador for one. The mountain tapir, too, is losing ground. Although it is protected in most places, the remoteness of much of its terrain makes it difficult to enforce a ban on hunting—poachers will always risk their lives to kill a wild animal if there is a price on its head. ■

*Although it lives in remote upland forests, the mountain tapir is gradually losing its homeland to hungry farmers and commercial logging companies.*

## ALONGSIDE MAN

### UNTAMED PRIDE

Domestic horses and asses have long formed an integral part of our history. But how successful have attempts been to tame zebras? European settlers used the quagga as a beast of burden, but they then caused its extinction with such rapidity that it is impossible to assess the success of this attempt at domestication.

Over the generations attempts have been made to use zebras as riding or draft animals but these have met with varying amounts of success. One settler in Cape Province was badly mauled by a pair of zebras when he tried to harness them to a cart. In the wild these animals are as vicious as any of the equids, and instinct tells them to elude capture. They are lighter than other equids in the forequarters, reducing their ability to carry a rider.

It seems that, in at least one instance, humans have been able to exploit zebras: They can be crossbred with horses and asses, although the offspring will be infertile. Zebroids—a cross between Grevy's zebra and a horse—have apparently been bred and used as beasts of burden in the Mount Kenya region, where they are claimed to be superior to mules and horses.

### ZEBRAS AND TAPIRS IN DANGER

THE CHART BELOW SHOWS HOW THE INTERNATIONAL UNION FOR THE CONSERVATION OF NATURE (IUCN), OR THE WORLD CONSERVATION UNION, CLASSIFIES THE STATUS OF ZEBRAS AND TAPIRS:

| | |
|---|---|
| MOUNTAIN ZEBRA | VULNERABLE |
| GREVY'S ZEBRA | ENDANGERED |
| BAIRD'S TAPIR | VULNERABLE |
| MOUNTAIN TAPIR | ENDANGERED |
| MALAYSIAN TAPIR | ENDANGERED |

ENDANGERED MEANS THAT THE ANIMAL'S SURVIVAL IS UNLIKELY UNLESS STEPS ARE TAKEN TO SAVE IT. VULNERABLE INDICATES THAT IT IS LIKELY TO MOVE INTO THE ENDANGERED CATEGORY IF THE SITUATION REMAINS UNIMPROVED.

# INTO THE FUTURE

It seems that so long as humans husband their resources carefully in Africa, all three species of zebra should survive. Numbers of the Cape mountain zebra are now probably sufficiently high to ensure its survival (see Mountain Success) and all species are protected legally. Aware of the intrinsic value of her rich wildlife, Africa has probably led the way in the establishment of national parks and reserves where animals live in a natural, but protected, environment, and all species of zebra exist in such parks. There is no longer any need to shoot these animals on the grounds that they are competing with domestic livestock for grazing. Such game hunting as there is is strictly controlled in accordance with numbers of animals in any given area.

All species of tapir probably face a gloomier future than the zebras. Since the turn of the last century the developing countries have lost nearly half of

## PREDICTION

### POPULATION PRESSURE

*The plains zebra is the most secure species of wild equid but it, too, will soon face the consequences of human pressure. There will be an estimated 720 million people living in Southeast Asia by 2020—almost double the population today.*

their forests and, although world awareness of this natural calamity is high, the destruction continues. Certainly in the Southeast Asian homelands of the Malayan tapir, and probably also in the ranges of the New World species, the predominant human activity is subsistence farming, which needs a constantly shifting program of cultivation. Thus peasant farmers continue to make inroads into the forest because there is nowhere else to go.

In some areas there has been a government policy to relocate overcrowded people to cleared forest areas; such is the case in Indonesia, where more than 3.5 million people have been moved, with another 65 million planned for transmigration over the next 20 years. This and many other similar projects were funded by the World Bank. In the 1970s, however, environmental groups began to lobby the bank to adopt more "green" policies. Today, the bank's projects must meet three criteria—economic growth, poverty alleviation, and environmental protection. Perhaps this powerful organization will now fight to save the world's forests, and the wildlife within. ∎

## MOUNTAIN SUCCESS

When the plight of the Cape mountain zebra became known in the 1930s, The National Parks Board of South Africa was spurred into action: It purchased a farm just northwest of Cradock, close to the south coast town of Port Elizabeth, and founded the Mountain Zebra National Park. Since then more farms have been added to the park, which now covers 16,385 acres (6,633 hectares).

About 200 Cape mountain zebras graze the land; this number is considered to be the maximum the area can support. The park is not served by bus or train, so the only way to visit is by car. In addition to zebras there is a proliferation of mountain reedbuck, klipspringers, steenboks, gemsboks, red hartebeests, and Karoo baboons, as well as ostriches and other birds.

## LIFE IN A WAR ZONE

*One factor that has clearly affected the animal life in many African countries in recent decades is war. When countries—and people—are being torn apart by conflict, the native wildlife is, understandably, low on their list of considerations. Conflict in Somalia may well have been partly responsible for the extermination of Grevy's zebra from this country, while military activity in Ethiopia, combined with drought, may also have furthered a decline in this zebra species.*

Illustration Evi Antoniou

# INDEX

Published by Marshall Cavendish Corporation
99 White Plains Road
Tarrytown, New York 10591-9001

© Marshall Cavendish Corporation, 1997
© Marshall Cavendish Ltd, 1994

The material in this series was first published in the English language by Marshall Cavendish Limited, of 119 Wardour Street, London W1V 3TD, England.

Library of Congress Cataloging-in-Publication Data

Encyclopedia of mammals.
p. cm.
Includes index.
ISBN 0-7614-0575-5 (set)    ISBN 0-7614-0591-7 (v. 16)

Summary: Detailed articles cover the history, anatomy, feeding habits, social structure, reproduction, territory,
and current status of ninety-five mammals around the world.
1. Mammals—Encyclopedias, Juvenile. [l. Mammals—Encyclopedias.]  I. Marshall Cavendish Corporation.
QL706.2.E54 1996
599'.003—dc20
                                                                    96-17736
                                                                    CIP
                                                                    AC

Printed in Malaysia
Bound in U.S.A.